BRAIN DAMAGE

Don't Learn to Live with It!

Margaret Baker
and Trevor England

Robinson Publishing

London

Robinson Publishing
7, Kensington Church Court
London W8 4SP

First published by Robinson Publishing 1993

A copy of the British Library Cataloguing in Publication
Data for this title is available from the British Library

ISBN 1 85487 179 X

Typeset by Hewer Text Composition Services, Edinburgh

Printed and bound by
HarperCollins Manufacturing, Glasgow

Contents

Foreword

In August 1980 my world came to a sudden standstill when my youngest child, Katy, was hit by a car. Although she had no obvious physical injuries, I was told that she had sustained a severe injury to her brain. She was in a coma, her chances of survival were sixty-forty against, and if she lived there was no way of knowing whether she would ever regain all her abilities.

I still vividly recall the horror of hearing that my bright, beautiful child might have been robbed of her future, and the overwhelming frustration of being powerless to do anything to help her other than wait, hope and pray. Luckily, I was introduced to people who made me understand the necessity of constant stimulation and a positive attitude, and since desperately busy hospital staff have little time for this her father and I undertook to provide it, instinctively feeling that our little girl would prefer to have us care for her than strangers. From that moment our sole purpose in life was to restore Katy to her former self. Our home became a caravan in the hospital grounds for six weeks before we were able to take her home to continue her therapy, and it was over a year before we could relax in the knowledge that she would be OK. We were lucky: our efforts and belief in Katy paid off and she made a complete recovery. Sadly, though, at any given time there are many, many more children suffering the consequences of brain injury, sustained before, during or after birth, with parents standing by as helpless as we were, desperate to do something positive.

This book has been written for those parents. It is not a medical textbook; it is written in language that parents will understand. It gives hope, but at the same time does not underestimate the problems that lie ahead. It provides some positive thoughts and reflections on what has so far been a negative situation and stresses that the future for a brain-damaged child need not always be as bleak as it is first painted. Most importantly of all, it gives parents the necessary advice, encouragement and opportunity to take control of their child's future, to do something positive to attempt to change the situation rather than simply learning to live with it. Had such a book existed at the time my daughter was injured it would have saved me both time and frustration.

I have been Patron of The Kerland Foundation since its inception in 1982. My own personal experience and my involvement with the Foundation have taught me that the battle against the effects of brain damage can be fought and won. My message to you is don't ever give up, don't lose hope and, above all, believe in your child.

Joan Collins
Patron of The Kerland Foundation

Introduction

The real-life story behind this book began just after the last war in Philadelphia, USA, when one of America's greatest war heroes returned to work. Glenn Doman was that man. He was a physical therapist who, in thanks for his deeds of gallantry, was presented with a ready-made practice on his return from the front. He settled down and became a respected and successful member of his profession. He also, perhaps through fate, renewed his relationship with one of the great neurosurgeons of all time – Temple Fay.

In a short time, the successful practice was gone and Glenn was immersed in what was to become a lifelong work – to try to eradicate the problems of children whom we call brain-injured and the outside world calls spastic, flaccid, cerebral-palsied, mongol, retarded, athetoid, autistic, subnormal.

The Institutes for the Achievement of Human Potential slowly evolved out of this work. A dedicated band of people – clinicians, psychologists, nurses – gave up their well-ordered lives to help Glenn Doman in his life's struggle to change the treatment of and approach to these children.

During the late 1960s and early 1970s, groups in the UK sent families to the Institutes for help but, for various reasons, their liaison did not last. In 1972, however, the father of a British child on their programme was asked by

Glenn to set up the British Institute for the Achievement of Human Potential (BIAHP). This he duly did, its first premises being Lanrick House in Stafford. All the initial assessments of the children were still carried out in America, with reassessments carried out by a team sent over from Philadelphia. In the period 1972–76, the BIAHP, under the directorship of John K. Pennock, grew at an amazing rate. Being a charity, it had the means to raise money, and this it did quite well. In 1976, with the help of a small loan from America, it moved to its present home at Knowle Hall. By 1978 it was working with 120 families and in 1979 it became independent of Philadelphia and changed its name to the British Institute of Brain Injured Children.

By 1981 the Institute was growing, in terms of both families and the amount of money raised. It was in that year that we – Margaret Baker, the Clinical Director, and Trevor England, the Appeals Director – decided that we no longer wanted to work at Knowle Hall because of fundamental differences between the way that the Institute was developing and the way in which we believed that it should develop. We resigned our posts in January 1982, and the Kerland Child Development Centre was born in March of the same year. Although we accepted the basic philosophies of the original Institutes for the Achievement of Human Potential, we decided to adapt and change them to suit the British way of life in five key ways:

1 We would carry out initial assessments with individual families at the centre. These would take two days and families would stay locally.
2 Reassessments would normally be carried out at the families' homes.
3 In general the time spent on the programme each day would be reduced.

4 We would try to work alongside the medical and educational systems rather than to replace them.

5 We would not restrict our work to children but would offer help to anyone who had suffered brain damage, with no restrictions whatsoever.

We have tried to learn from the criticisms directed at this type of work, although many are unfounded and based on hearsay. We are the first to admit that we do not know all the answers to what we should do with each and every family. We do know, however, that we are experiencing encouraging successes with many children whom the system had given up on. One interesting observation has been made: during the 1970s the British Institute was always the last resort, families arriving there after they had tried everything else; today the children are arriving at a younger age. It appears that families who do not want to accept a bleak future for their child are finding out very quickly about this type of therapy – that in itself is considerable progress.

From the results that we see being attained we are hopeful that in our lifetime people's attitudes towards the brain-injured, and how they should be treated, and what they can achieve, will undergo a dramatic change. Unfortunately, however, very little information is easily available to families about the options available to help the brain-injured. We wrote this book because families need to know what has gone wrong when someone is brain-injured. They also need encouragement and help in taking positive steps to improve the quality of life of their loved one. We have described the methods that we use at the Kerland Clinic and the rationale behind them in the hope that our book will help families come to a decision about the best treatment for their children, partners or parents.

Chapter 1

Is this a new beginning?

What is brain damage?

Every year in the UK, and in every other country in the world, thousands of children are born brain-damaged. In many cases this is the result of a problem during birth; in others the child is genetically impaired, or is damaged soon after birth by a virus. Others suffer vaccine damage or are injured by a car accident or drowning. Moreover, growing numbers of children and adults suffer brain damage as a result of strokes.

Dead brain cells cannot be brought back to life, but children and adults with injured or damaged brains can be treated with a wide variety of therapies, in the course of which they may develop or regain functional abilities. For children, it is now accepted that those who receive stimulation in early infancy make significant improvements compared with those who receive regular physiotherapy alone.

Treatment options and resources

Huge amounts of resources are needed for proper rehabilitation programmes in all our towns and cities but there is a growing shortfall in what is available. The *Working Party*

Report of the Medical Disability Society (1988) highlighted this problem. It pointed out that the incidence of brain injury is forty times that of spinal injury but that there are many more spinal and orthopaedic units within our medical system than those intended for the sole use of the victims of brain injury. This continuing problem highlights the lack of resources devoted to the treatment of brain damage and also the attitudes of many within the National Health Service.

Our stretched NHS struggles manfully with the problem but, all too frequently, when a case of brain injury is no longer acute it is the parents and families who are left to bear the brunt of coping with, in many cases, a barely alive individual whom they love dearly. Rather than give up and accept the situation, the parents and loved one begin a confused and unguided search for help, initially within the NHS and educational systems. Eventually, however, the search takes them outside what is generally available free.

It takes time for the parents or family to reach this stage. Initially at least, they accept the hospital management of their loved one as treatment and their hopes are raised. Here we come to one of the problems that we must overcome: can we ever expect to *treat* injured brains or is the best we can do simply to *manage* the effects of the condition? Many professionals in the field now appear to have given up hope of trying to solve the neurological problems by remedial methods. They have stopped looking for positive results and have become critical of organisations outside the NHS that may achieve results.

Doctors often do not have the time to talk to families and carers about the reasons for and consequences of their decisions. For example, sometimes surgery is performed merely to make life easier for the family or carers, not as a remedy for the brain injury. In our experience, explanations are rarely given about the long-term effects of surgery, which may make care easier but rehabilitation almost impossible.

Furthermore, insufficient information is given about the progress that can be expected of a brain-injured child. If a child is born with brain injury, normal development through a rehabilitative programme will usually be impossible: for example, the doctor may not expect that the child will ever walk but this is not always made clear to the parents.

Parents almost inevitably eventually look elsewhere to get the best for their child. This affects several relationships – medical and educational professionals to family, family to child – and the motivation and morale of everyone are seriously affected. Many parents are left with the belief that there is nothing available in the UK – but this is wrong. Much of what is available is good and staffed by committed people: there are simply not enough facilities and money to provide what is necessary for these families on a daily basis within the NHS. Furthermore, parents or families have not been thought of as potential therapists. Now, in the 1990s, there are signs of change – but not enough. It is our belief that parents and friends can be the best therapists if taught and monitored properly. They can handle both the management and the treatment of any form of therapy.

What are the alternatives?

When families begin to look for therapy outside the traditional system, they often feel unsupported and even ostracised by the medical, educational and social systems. They are trying to do the best for their loved ones and, sadly, do not have much faith in many of the professionals that they have seen. They may be shunted from consultant to consultant, hospital to hospital, at a time when treatment is imperative if good results are to be achieved.

6

Is this a new beginning?

So where do families find out about 'alternative' therapies? The popular press has helped glamorise places like the Peto Clinic in Hungary and the Institutes for the Achievement of Human Potential in Philadelphia. At the Kerland Clinic we get some referrals from hospitals but most people hear about us by word of mouth or from information that we supply to libraries and other organisations.

It is important to remember that several effective modes of therapy can be employed by the NHS, individual therapists and the families themselves. Unfortunately, there is a great deal of polarisation among those who practise particular therapies. Many practitioners think that their way is right and everyone else is wrong. This is not necessarily true, but when families try to pick what they consider to be the best ideas from a variety of therapies, this leads to poor results and even more confusion.

In the end, it is up to the individual family or parent to decide what they feel is the best therapy for their loved one. However, to do this the information must be made available to them and they need to understand the full implications of whatever therapeutic approach they are setting out on. It is also difficult and confusing to transplant a therapeutic approach developed in one country to another country.

In addition to the approach adopted by the Kerland Clinic, which will be described in this book, other types of therapy are available in Europe. Some of them are listed below.

Vaglav Voyta, of Czechoslovakia and Germany, is now based in Cologne. His work involves reflex crawling and other triggered reactions based probably on the work of Temple Fay.

Berta and Karmel Bobath, very much in vogue in London

in the 1960s, appeared to lose direction in the 1970s and early 1980s, perhaps because of the glamour associated with other styles of therapy.

Andreas Peto's Conductive Education has found success in Hungary. Parts of his system are being applied as a method of rehabilitation in the UK but without the success achieved in Hungary. Dr Sutton of Birmingham University is currently engaged in a project to import the method in its original detail from Hungary.

The *Doman-Delacato* programme had a high profile and Doman himself in the 1970s and early 1980s was extremely critical of the 'system'. This style of rehabilitation therapy has therefore had far greater exposure to criticism than others. In 1975 Beasley and Hagarty of Keele University carried out a study of British children attending the Philadelphia institute. More recently, Cummins (1988) has attempted to bury the Doman-Delcato system of intensive therapy conducted by parents and friends on an outpatient basis.

The Kerland Clinic

At the Kerland Clinic we have based our work on the system developed by Doman and Delacato at the Institutes for the Achievement of Human Potential in Philadelphia, as we described in the Introduction. We believe that their ideas are basically correct except in their application. We do not believe in long, all-day every-day programmes; we do not believe in elitism; we do believe in research to substantiate our work; we do believe that our programmes of fifteen hours per week can be carried out alongside what the health and education systems offer. (Interestingly, Delacato, who left the Philadelphia institute in the early 1970s, has also developed a shorter programme, which he believes is most effective.)

Can you prove that the Kerland method works?

To our knowledge, no one has attempted to review the Kerland therapy, although we are hoping in the next few years to develop several research projects with a major British university to review the events of the last ten years.

It is, in our opinion, easy to define successes: they are readily demonstrated by our records, both written and videotaped. However, it is far more difficult to define failure, and it is to this area that we must address ourselves. Over the last ten years we have had some outstanding successes with children and we have had some complete failures, but the vast majority of children are in the middle band, where improvements in development are not dramatic but are nevertheless steady. It is only the families themselves who can answer the question of whether the improvement was worth the effort: we are sure that most would say yes because, after all, what is the alternative?

We have been using our own very crude developmental graph to chart the progress of each patient. These graphs, together with video data of the patient, highlight the great problems in trying to set up acceptable research protocols.

We have also had access to a magnetic resonance imaging facility on site: this technique is used to 'scan' the brain and produce an image of it. The child's own doctor formally requests a scan, and the report is returned to the doctor for evaluation. We have, however, met with some very contentious opinions about the use of scanning technology to examine brain-injured children and adults. Scans at present can determine only the physical extent of the brain damage, and very few follow-up scans are done because of the costs involved. We think that scanning technology can determine whether it is wise to try any rehabilitation therapy, but decisions should be based only on a gross lack of brain tissue from whatever cause. We have seen, for example, scans of children and adults who have only 20–30 per cent of the normal brain structure but who are leading a normal life, holding down jobs, getting married and so on. Others apparently show a normal brain structure but it is clear that there is a problem because the patient is barely alive. To date, we have found no way of determining whether a programme of therapy would be successful simply by using technological information. Although some of the newer scanning techniques, such as the positron emission tomography or PET scanner, might help, again the costs preclude their use in brain-damaged patients. More research clearly needs to be done in this area, but in the future scans may be able to give us invaluable information.

There is, therefore, no easy way of telling who will benefit from treatment. We have to accept that we will always have failures and that we must continually search for answers to our failures. It is no good simply wishing and hoping: we must devote a growing percentage of time to learning, developing and using better techniques, and to looking at ways of improving our approach. It is apparent that here is an excellent case for better co-operation between medical professionals and families who have a brain-injured child. Although everyone agrees that resources are inadequate, doctors and physiotherapists should take the time to learn more about our work. Sadly, we have had far more interest from professionals in a small country such as Finland than from those in the UK. Kerland is available for all families who are prepared to work hard, beyond the basic demands of caring, and who understand that, despite their efforts, they may not get the results that they want, or indeed any result at all.

Conclusion

Information about all the treatment options should be made available to families so that, with counselling, they can decide whether they want to try a particular therapy. Much of the Kerland approach can be used alongside other available resources. Sadly, however, it is only those families who are prepared to travel, to find volunteers and to use their own cash who will probably achieve a measure of change in their loved one. We can help only a small percentage of families, but that number is growing as many parents or partners refuse to accept what they are told and do not give up hope.

We might be accused of being over-critical of the medical profession. However, we must realise that, with an average doctor-patient contact of only seven minutes per consultation, we cannot expect communication to be easy. Moreover, many professionals appear not to value the involvement of the parent or partner and some even consider anyone who questions their decisions or prognosis as 'difficult'.

There is little doubt that the diagnosis of disabling conditions is difficult in adults and even more so in young children. Long-term consequences of brain injury are difficult to predict and many families receive negative opinions about the potential progress of their loved ones. It becomes obvious that the outcome of any rehabilitative process is largely dependent on the attitude of the primary carers (usually the families): they particularly need a sense of optimism and a willingness not to accept what they have been told.

We believe that the views of the medical and educational establishment must change; research into our methods must be positive; criticism must be positive and not based on third- or fourth-hand information. The problem is one of communication and understanding, not of criticism and bigotry. Only by communication and discussion can we help those families who want to be helped in our way.

Chapter 2

How should my child have developed?

The development of 'normal' children has some bearing on the problems that we face with brain-injured children. It is our firm belief that, rather than developing along abnormal lines, the brain-injured child follows normal patterns of development in all areas of function until he reaches a block. This block may appear so early that it prevents the child from developing any ability in one of the areas, or so late that for several years the parents are unaware that a problem exists. The block may occur in one or two of the areas of function or at a different stage in each area, but in each case the child reaches a level of normal development and then stops.

If we can ascertain the point at which development stopped, then we can see the next level we have to strive for. If the child is to succeed in life, then he must ultimately go through all the normal stages of development. The six essential areas of development are:

1 The development of vision
2 The development of hearing and understanding
3 The development of touch and sensation
4 The development of mobility
5 The development of language
6 The development of hand function

In this chapter we shall explain how these areas of function develop in the 'normal' child and then in the next chapters we shall show how the stages of development are blocked – and can be unblocked – in brain-injured children.

Development of vision

Visual development covers the span between the purely reflexive constriction of the pupil in response to light and the ability to read and comprehend complex pieces of literature.

At the time of birth, the baby is not consciously able to see anything but should have a very efficient light reflex. When a light is shone into the baby's eyes, the dark circle in the centre of the eye, known as the pupil, instantly contracts to the size of a pin-head. Similarly, when the light is removed, the pupil dilates, that is becomes larger. At this stage, the baby is not actually seeing formed images, but the reflex shows that the presence and absence of light is registering on the brain. The alteration in the size of the pupil simply controls the amount of light allowed through to stimulate the brain. We think it important at this stage to point out that in many cases the efficiency of the light reflex has little to do with the ability to see. We have known children with extremly acute vision to have a very sluggish light reflex – the pupil contracts very slowly or to nowhere near the size of a pin-head – simply because of the amount of drugs they are taking to control fits or hyperactivity. In direct opposition to this we have seen children with perfect reactions of the pupil but who are obviously unable to see.

At the next level, the baby begins to see the difference between light and dark, and becomes strongly attracted to light. The baby at this stage of development will often turn his head towards a brightly lit window, or will look up towards a light when it is switched on. Bright colours reflect light and it is for this reason that many parents will note their babies gazing fixedly at something red or yellow. As well as being able to tell the difference between light and dark, the baby at this level is beginning to make out vague outlines, particularly where there is a strong contrast of light. If an object or person passes between his face and the light source, his eyes will briefly follow it, and if a hand is passed in front of his eyes, fairly closely to his face, he will blink. It is also easy at this stage to attract his attention with a torch or flickering match in a dark room, and he may even be able to follow it briefly from side to side. We would like to stress that at this level of visual development, known as outline perception, the child does not know what he is seeing but is simply aware that something is there. An easy way to understand this is to go into a dark, unfamiliar room. As your eyes become accustomed to the dark you are aware of objects situated around you, but cannot see exactly what they are. Of course you can make an educated guess based on past experience, but remember the baby does not have any past visual experience, and therefore he cannot even guess.

From here, the baby progresses to being able to see in greater detail, that is, to being able to recognise certain people and objects, although to begin with this is very hazy. For example, he will be able to recognise a particular face. A recent experience made it easier for one of us to understand this level of vision. I was a passenger in a car in the rain and the windscreen wiper on the passenger side was broken. I was able to see enough to make out cars and people, but not enough to be able to tell the make of car or whether the person was male or female, old or young. This is a very difficult stage, as you have to work really hard in order to understand what you are seeing, and eventually I found it easier not to bother trying. In the same way, I am sure that children at this level also 'switch off' from time to time, with the result that parents will worry that sometimes the child seems to be aware of his surroundings, but at other times will appear not really to see anything. As the baby progresses through this level, however, his ability to see becomes more consistent until he can pick out his mother's face from a group of people, will take off across the room for a favourite toy, and will stop crying as soon as he sees his bottle appear on the scene. At this point the child has truly become a sighted human being.

Until now all the stages of vision we have discussed have entailed the baby using only one eye at a time. This does not mean that he is only able to see with one eye, or that the vision in one eye is better than that in the other. It simply means that the brain has not yet reached the level of maturity required for both eyes to be used together. When we look at an object, each eye sees a separate image. Until the next level of visual development, known as *convergence*, has been reached, usually at about twelve months, the brain is unable to cope with these two images, so it simply cuts out one of them. In most cases this will alternate and the baby will tend to use his right eye to look at objects towards the right side and vice versa. This is known as *monocular vision*, and results in everything the child sees appearing flat – that is, he is not yet able to appreciate the third dimension. When convergence develops the brain is able to fix together the two individual images to form one, and for the first time the baby has the ability to perceive depth. An interesting exercise you might like to do to help you better understand this concept is as follows. Close one eye and look around the room. Pick out one object in the room and line it up with something else close by – either another object to the side of it or a wall or piece of furniture behind it. Now try and estimate the distance between the two. When you open the other eye you will be surprised how much you misjudged that distance. As the ability to see with only one eye at a time is known as monocular vision, so the ability to see with both eyes together is known as *binocular vision*.

As previously stated, the baby is now already able to recognise favourite toys, objects and people. The next stage of development is for him to be able to recognise these same things in picture form.

From here on, it is not so much a question of how well he sees but more one of how well he understands and interprets what he sees. From pictures, he will go on to recognise shapes, symbols and letters and eventually to be able to read words.

Development of hearing and understanding

Auditory competence covers the span between the newborn baby's first reaction to sound and his ability to comprehend the spoken word when used in a highly complex sentence structure.

Within moments of birth, a baby will react to a sudden loud noise close by. This reaction can vary from simply a visible increase in respiration rate or a fluttering of the eyelids to a pronounced eye blink or in some cases a whole body jerk. At this stage the baby has no understanding of the noise, nor is he particularly disturbed by it. It is purely a reflex reaction indicating that the noise has registered on his brain. This level of hearing is known as the startle reflex.

When the baby reaches the next level, known as vital response to threatening sounds, his reaction is of a more conscious nature. Now instead of merely blinking or jumping to show that the sound has been heard, he is likely to be frightened or upset, which will often result in him crying. Common examples of this are the baby who cries when a car horn is sounded too close to his pram, or the baby who wakes up crying when a door is slammed or a child shouts. The baby at this stage of development still has no understanding of the sounds, which largely explains his reason for being frightened by them. You can imagine how you yourself would feel if whilst out walking on a quiet road you suddenly heard a siren-like noise that you had never heard before. Your immediate reaction would be one of fear and apprehension until you were able to track down the source of the sound and give some rational explanation for it.

As the baby moves into the next step, the sounds he hears begin to take on more meaning. Often the first indication of this is that the mother speaks reassuringly to her crying baby as she goes to pick him up and suddenly realises that he has stopped crying before she has reached him. Although the baby has not understood the meaning of the words his mother used, he has understood the music of them – he recognises the tone of her voice as being warm, soothing and comforting. In the same way, a baby at this level will often burst into tears if his mother scolds or speaks sharply to another child. The actual words used to a baby at this level are immaterial; it is the way in which they are said that conveys the meaning. For instance, you can say to your baby, 'You are a very naughty boy and I'm going to smack you,' and provided you say it in a warm, soft voice with a smile on your face, your child will smile and gurgle contentedly. On the other hand, you can tell him that he is a wonderful baby and you absolutely adore him, but if you say this in a stern voice and frown, the chances are that he will promptly burst into tears. It is at this time that the baby also begins to recognise certain voices, particularly those of his parents. Along with this he will begin to recognise certain sounds within his environment. A baby who enjoys being bathed will squeal with excitment at the sounds of running water; a hungry baby will stop grizzling when he hears the clink of a spoon against a dish; he will turn in anticipation towards a door when somebody rings a bell; he will join in

17

the general laughter of adults around him, and the sound of another baby crying may produce tears of sympathy. By now the baby will also be more adept at localising the sound, being able to tell the direction from which it comes, and will readily turn towards the source of the sound.

At the next level of auditory development the child is beginning to comprehend the meaning of the words spoken rather than just the tone of voice. As a rule the first word to mean anything to him will be his name, as this will be the one that is said directly to him most of all. This is often closely followed by a consistent response to the word 'no', as again he will frequently hear this when he goes to touch something that is out of bounds. Generally, the first words to take on any specific meaning to the child are those that he hears the most often, such as family names and names of favourite toys, but he is really still only able to understand single words, and picks out these key words from the general jumble that he hears. For instance, you may say to him, 'Go and pick teddy up,' and off he crawls to pick up his favourite toy. The only word that really registered with him was teddy, but this was enough to set off a whole string of reactions. Those of you who know a smattering of a foreign language will be familiar with this concept, because you will know the feeling of listening for one word that you recognise so that you can grasp the general gist of what is being said.

From this stage it is no time at all until the baby is able to recognise and understand simple phrases, such as 'put it down' or 'wave bye bye'. From here on, at about eighteen months, his understanding will escalate at a terrific rate. Compare the rate at which a two-year-old learns the meaning of new words and phrases with the rate at which you could do the same with a foreign language and you will be amazed. Remember that to the baby English is as much a foreign language as Russian is to you. It is important to note at this point that no child is taught every word that he understands, but that he picks up the vast majority from hearing them in everyday usage. For instance, how many times does he have to hear such phrases as 'don't touch the fire' and 'come away from the fire' and 'the fire will burn you', before he realises that the thing mum keeps moving him away from is called a fire? She may use a different sentence each time, but the common factor will be the word 'fire'.

At this stage of development the child is very much concerned with the present. It is no use to tell him in the morning that you will take him to the park in the afternoon, because he has no concept of time. All he understands is that you are going to take him to the park and as far as he is concerned that means right now. By the end of this stage the child will have an extensive vocabulary of words and sentences that he understands. He will also be able to carry out a large number of simple directions, such as 'take it to daddy', 'close the door', provided they are given to him one at a time.

From here on, as with visual development, it is mainly a question of sophistication. By the age of three years, the child will be able to cope with two directions given at the same time such as 'go and get your shoes and bring them to me', and this ability will expand until he is able to follow through several steps. He will begin to comprehend the concept of time, beginning by understanding that 'in a few minutes' means 'not right now', going through the phase of knowing that 'tomorrow' means after he has been to bed, and eventually grasping the relevance of 'next week' and even 'next year'. He will also begin to listen to speech that is not directed at him, and a mother may find that when she casually mentions to her husband that they should go out for a ride in the car, her child is already at the door complete with coat and shoes. It is at this stage that mum usually finds herself spelling out things that she does not want the child to hear. She will also find that when she is quietly passing on some amusing snippet of conversation, her child, who is to all intents and purposes fully absorbed in a jig-saw puzzle, is equally amused. As development in this area continues, the child acquires a degree of judgement, which enables him to anticipate the consequences of certain actions and to be aware of elements of risk and danger. He will also have a good idea of what is acceptable and what is not. Auditory competence in the sense of understanding is really an area of development which continues throughout life. We are constantly being presented with new thoughts and ideas, and a measure of intelligence is directly related to the ability to grasp and comprehend their significance in order to reach a rational conclusion about their worth.

Development of touch and sensation

The development of tactile competence covers the span between the baby's first reflex response and the sophisticated ability to identify unfamiliar objects with the fingertips.

Most small babies seem to be aware of being held and touched, but one very sound way of testing his tactile awareness is known as the Babinski reflex. If the side of the foot is stroked firmly from the heel towards the toes, the toes will react reflexively. This is a reflex which persists throughout life, but which changes in characteristic during the first year of life. Initially the baby will respond by raising his big toe, and the rest of his toes will fan out. This is known as a positive Babinski reflex. However, somewhere between the sixth and twelfth month of life this response will change, and when the same stimulation is given the toes will all curl downwards. This is known as either a negative Babinski or a normal planter reflex.

The next level, known as vital sensation, is when the baby begins to be consciously aware of pain. This becomes apparent when he is taken for his first vaccination, at which he screams loud and long. He will also cry out if his first suck at the bottle provides him with milk that is too hot, and similarly if a spoon happens to touch gums that are tender from teething. Indeed, if teething took place before this level of tactile development, there would be far fewer sleepless nights.

At the next stage of development, the baby begins to be aware of tactile stimulation of a less intensive nature. This is known as the development of gnostic sensation. At this stage the baby chortles with delight when being tickled and can often be soothed to sleep by a gentle stroking of his head or back. He is also becoming more selective about what he eats on the grounds that he is now more sensitive to temperature and may prefer warm food to cold, or vice versa. This sensitivity may carry over to the baby liking his bath water to be a certain temperature, or to be irritated by woollen clothing next to the skin. As he progresses through this level the baby's sensitivity increases to the degree that if a fly should land on his leg he is instantly aware of its exact location. Along with the awareness of light touch the baby also begins to be aware of different textures, and will pat and stroke different surfaces, usually with the palm of his hand. It is likely that he will have strong preferences for some textures over others, and may vehemently reject some toys simply because he cannot tolerate the feel of them.

By the time he reaches the next level, the baby is beginning to experiment more with his hands. Whereas until now he has tended to touch everything with the flat of his hand he now begins to bring his fingers into the action. The baby lying on a blanket on the floor will run his hand across the surface until he reaches the edge, but now his fingers are sensitive enough to recognise the change in surface and he will curl his fingers around the edge of the blanket. Similarly, while stroking mum's hair, which appears to be flat, he will recognise by the feel of it that again he can curl his fingers around it – so enabling him to give a good tug which is guaranteed to produce a suitable reaction from her. At this stage of development the baby no longer needs to look at an object in order to pick it up. His tactile awareness is now sufficient to tell him when his hand has alighted on something that can be grasped, although he would not yet know exactly what he was holding on to.

As he moves on to the next stage this ability becomes more sophisticated and now the baby is able to recognise certain familiar objects by feeling them without seeing them. An example of this is a baby who wakes in a dark room and feels around the assortment of toys and pillows in his cot until he finds his dummy. His hand will instantly close on this, and with luck he pops it into his mouth and settles down to sleep again. The child at this level will also rummage deep into his toy box and emerge with his favourite battered teddy bear which was hidden away under the pile. If a biscuit or a piece of bread is put into his hand, he instantly knows that this is something to eat as opposed to something to cast aside.

By the time he reaches the end of this stage the child is using the ability on a wider variety of objects. As he passes into the next level, his fingers are telling him much more about the objects he is feeling, including those that are unfamiliar to him. He will not be able to name them, but will certainly attempt to describe them or to liken them to other familiar objects. For instance, if a hair curler is put into his hand it is unlikely that he will know what it is, but he is highly likely to be able to tell you that it is prickly. Similarly if a large wooden bead is placed in his hand he may tell you that it is a ball, because it closely resembles an object that he is used to handling.

From here on, as with the other areas, it is a question of sophistication. The child becomes more able to identify objects rather than merely describe them, including items that he may never have felt before. For instance, he may be familiar with paper clips to the degree that he has seen them holding papers together and has been told what they are called but has never handled one. While groping around in a box or drawer, he may come across one, and by examining it carefully between his fingers and thumbs he is able to conjure up a visual image, which instantly tells him what it is. We are constantly putting this ability into use, probably without realising it. How many times do you see a man reach into a pocket probably of loose change and come out with the precise coin he wants, or a woman dive deep into a bulging handbag and surprisingly emerge with the one small object she is seeking?

Development of mobility

The development of mobility ranges from the baby's first aimless movements of his arms and legs to the abilities of running, skipping and kicking a ball.

When the baby is born he has a complete range of movement in all four limbs. These movements are very much of a random nature and do not involve any movement of the body itself. The baby is most likely to demonstrate this ability when crying, when he appears to be striking and grasping at the air. At this stage the baby's movement cannot in any way be called purposeful, although later he will kick his legs and wave his arms about for the sheer joy it gives him.

In order to reach the next stage of commando crawling, which is moving across the floor on his tummy in a cross pattern, several things must happen. The first and most obvious thing is that the baby must be put on his tummy. When this happens, those same aimless, random movements instantly become purposeful. Now instead of striking at the air, the baby's limbs are moving against the floor, and providing he is given enough opportunity to do this, they will soon become strong enough to make these movements propulsive in nature so that they carry him forward. The first real sign of movement that you are likely to see, however, is that the baby moves round in a circle. Most mums tend to put their babies down on a rug or a blanket, and the day will dawn when mum looks in to check on him and finds that although her baby is still in the same place, he is facing the opposite direction. The next step will be that he will start to wriggle backwards, and the final achievement of this level of development is that he begins to move forward. At first this will be in an ungainly fashion – very much hit and miss, in that the majority of his movements will still be random with only the occasional one actually taking him forward. However, these purposeful movements soon become consistent and controlled until eventually he moves across the floor at considerable speed, in a smooth, well-synchronised cross-pattern flow of movement, pushing forward with his left leg at the same time as pulling with his right arm and vice versa. We believe that it is essential for a baby to have some experience of this level of mobility, however brief, in order to achieve the next level of crawling on hands and knees. Some mothers would adamantly protest that their babies never have done this, but it is probable that those babies performed this function to some degree during the night. Every mother is familiar with the experience of going in to check on the sleeping baby to find him wedged in the corner of his cot with his head pressed against the rails. It is those same movements of commando crawling that have taken him there, and although she may move him back into the centre of the cot the chances are that before long he will again have worked himself up into the corner.

As mentioned earlier, the next level of development is crawling on hands and knees, with the body raised from the floor. In order to achieve this level, the baby has to defy gravity for the first time in his life. The movements involved in commando crawling will have given his limbs the strength needed to support his body, but now he will also need some degree of balance. It is much more precarious to have just four points of contact with the floor rather than the whole surface of your body, and when the baby is actually moving he will at any given time have only two points of contact. The first step towards this level is that when the baby is commando crawling, you will from time to time see his bottom raised in the air – usually in an attempt to achieve greater speed of movement. The next step is that the baby actually pushes himself up onto his hands and knees, but once there is stuck. If he wants to move forwards, he has first of all to lower himself down onto his tummy again. From here he soon moves to a point where, having got himself onto his hands and knees, he begins to rock backwards and forwards. What he is actually doing is experimenting with shifting his weight and maintaining his balance, in order to be capable of taking the next step of lifting one hand and the opposite knee and moving a pace forward. Once he has mastered this he is virtually able to crawl, and again this will be a cross-pattern movement. Once he has achieved this level of mobility, a whole new world opens up for the baby. Those of you who have had the experience of chasing a determined baby heading off across a large open space on his hands and knees will realise what an efficient means of transportation this is. The baby can now be said to be well and truly mobile.

The next level of mobility for the baby to reach is walking with his arms in the primary balance position – that is with hands at shoulder level – but once again there are several stages he must go through before this is achieved. The first time he gets onto his feet is generally when he pulls himself up from hands and knees with the help of a piece of furniture

– often the leg of a table so that he can see what is on the top. Once he reaches this stage, nothing is safe unless it is placed out of his reach; parents often under-estimate the length of the baby's arms and just how far he is able to reach. Once able to stand in this way, the baby soon realises that he is able to side-step along the piece of furniture, using the arms of the chair or the edge of the coffee table for support. At first, when he reaches the end of the table or chair, he will let himself down onto his hands and knees, crawl to the next piece of furniture, and pull himself up again, but before long he will be brave enough to move from one piece to another while still on his feet as long as they are close enough so that he does not have to leave go of the first in order to reach for the second. This is, in fact, the next step, that he will for a matter of seconds be standing independently while he shifts his weight to move him from the chair towards the table, while keeping both feet firmly planted on the floor, and it may be some time before he develops the confidence to actually take a step. The age at which babies walk ranges between ten and eighteen months. Before he takes off and walks by himself the baby usually goes through a stage of cruising, where he is able to walk virtually all around the home by moving from one piece of furniture to another, and when none is available to walk with his hands flat against the wall. From here the natural next step is that he turns from the wall and walks across the open space to mum, with feet wide apart and hands at shoulder level to help him balance. He is unable to stop until he either reaches a person or piece of furniture or falls over. Although the baby now has the ability to walk, usually if he wants to get somewhere in a hurry he will revert to crawling, as this is still a more efficient means of moving for him. The child can be said to be a walker when he abandons crawling and uses the upright position for all transportation.

The next level of mobility is reached when the child is

able to walk without using his arms for balance – that is, he keeps his arms down by his sides or can walk whilst carrying an object. Now he will be able to stop walking, stand still, then continue, and will develop the ability to bend down, pick something up from the floor, and stand up again without losing his balance. As his ability to walk improves, you will begin to see that he again moves in a cross-pattern, as with the lower levels of mobility. This becomes apparent when the child begins to swing his arms, as the right arm will swing forwards as he steps out with his left foot and vice versa. All people walk in this pattern, and if you consciously try to walk moving your left arm at the same time as your left foot, you will find it extremely difficult.

The next level in the development of mobility is running, which again will be in a cross-pattern. While building up to this, the child will develop what is known as a fast walk. The difference between this and running is that with walking one foot remains in contact with the ground at all times, which means that one foot is not raised from the ground until the other one has been put down. With running however, with each step, the child has to momentarily leave the ground with both feet at the same time. When the child first begins to run, it will be with no apparent pattern, and indeed you may for a short time see his arms return to being held at shoulder level as his balance is threatened until he has mastered this ability. As he progresses through this stage, the cross-pattern will become evident and his arms will be held at waist level and used in a pumping action to provide greater speed.

From here, all that remains is for the child to develop the more sophisticated physical abilities of jumping, skipping, hopping and kicking a ball. It is then a question of both opportunity and desire to take these activities further, into the realms of gymnastics, sports and dance, up to levels required for either simply recreation or serious competition.

Development of language

The development of language covers the span between the baby's first cry at the moment of birth, and the ability to hold a fluent and rational conversation.

Within moments of birth, the baby cries for the first time. This first cry does not simply announce his arrival in the world, but is a vital reflex to indicate spontaneous breathing. At this stage, the crying is for no conscious reason on the part of the baby.

Before long, the next level is reached and the baby's ability to cry ceases to be purely reflex. It is used to indicate distress, usually when he experiences pain, hunger, or discomfort. For the time being, crying is his only means of communication.

As the baby moves into the next stage, he is able to create more varied sounds and they become more meaningful in nature. The first sign of this is usually that mum detects different tones in her baby's crying, and she soon becomes an expert at determining his urgency. For example, she will instantly know if the cry is an indication of pain or fear, and will fly to his assistance, but if it is just a way of saying 'I'm bored and want attention', she is more likely to call out to him and finish what she is doing before going to investigate. Similarly, all mothers are familiar with the cry that tells them that the baby is in need of sleep. It is during this stage that the baby really becomes aware of his voice and the use to which he can put it. New sounds will begin to emerge so that he is better able to express his emotions. If somebody claps their hands and makes a face, he will laugh, whilst if they tickle him he will squeal with delight. Similarly, he will shout with annoyance but will actually scream with anger. He will learn that if he puts his lips together he can produce a 'm' or 'b' sound but that his tongue to the roof of his mouth produces a 'd' sound. Also, putting his tongue out and blowing will produce a beautiful 'raspberry'. The mother will not need to see her baby in order to determine his mood; she will be able to tell when he is outside in his pram if he is happy, bored or in pain, simply by listening. While all these sounds are developing, the baby will also be aware of the effect they have on people. For instance, he will soon learn that a piercing scream will instantly bring mum running, while happy gurgles and squeals will keep him the centre of attention for hours. Raspberries will produce laughter and shocked expressions, while a bad-tempered wail will earn him sharp words or even a rap on the bottom. Once the baby has completed this stage of development, he is able to command his audience.

The next stage of development is reached usually around his first birthday, when the baby is able to say one or two recognisable words of speech. In the vast majority of cases, the first word a baby will be heard to say is 'mama'. It is important that you understand that when he first utters this sound, the baby has absolutely no idea of what he is saying; he is merely experimenting with sound. However, every mother on the face of the earth, on hearing this, is convinced that her baby is saying her name. Her reaction is one of total joy, and the child, feeling very pleased with himself, repeats it. If anybody else is around, mum is likely to say, 'Did you hear him he said "mama",' and from that moment on every time he makes the sound she responds to him. Obviously, it is no time at all before the baby realises that every time he produces this sound, his mother appears, and before long he uses it deliberately when he wants her. He now has his first word of speech, and has learned that a specific sound will bring about a consistent response. From now on, new sounds will be assigned to all manner of objects within his environment, although for some time only those close to him will understand their meaning.

For instance, a stranger hearing the baby make the sound 'ed' may respond by saying 'yes, there's your head' when his mother knows that in fact the child is asking for his teddy.

The stage to follow this is usually quickly reached, and this is when the child begins to put two words together. Whereas until now he has been able to say both 'bye-bye' and 'dada' as separate words, he will one morning surprise his father by saying 'bye-bye dada'. It now becomes easier for him to produce new sounds, and during this level the child is likely to try to repeat everything he hears, although many times the words that emerge will differ somewhat from those that he heard. For example, 'clap hands' usually gets translated into something like 'cappans'. He is also now likely to repeat the last couple of words of everything that is said to him and to fill in the last word of the line of a nursery rhyme that he has heard many times. His vocabulary at this time seems to increase more quickly than at any other time in his development.

From here, it is a gradual progression from linking two words to stringing together three or four until eventually the child is speaking in short sentences. To begin with these sentences will contain the strangest combinations of tenses with some made-up words as the child tries to sort out the rules of language. For instance, a child reporting his grandmother's visit of the day before may say, 'Granny comed to see us the last day'. The best way for the child to learn the correct structure is for mum to repeat the sentence properly: 'Yes, Granny came to see us yesterday.' That is in fact the way in which most children eventually come up with a reasonable form of English.

Very few parents are heard to say, 'No, that's not the way you say it, you are supposed to say it like this.' If this were to happen it would take all day to get through the simplest conversations.

As with all the other areas of development already discussed, the final stages of this area are a matter of sophistication. As his speech becomes more understandable, so people will respond more appropriately to him, and he will begin to correct his own mistakes. In the earlier levels of development, the child will have been dependent on an adult who could interpret what he is saying, but as time goes by he will be able to converse with other children. Language is a fascinating subject, especially when you bear in mind that when we start a sentence, invariably we have no more than a vague idea how we are going to finish it. Yet other people can follow the same line of thought to the degree that if we omitted a word, they could supply it. For instance, if I say, 'English is the most complex of all spoken . . .,' how many of you have not by now filled in the word 'languages'? My guess would be not many.

Development of hand function

The development of manual competence covers the span between the baby's first reflex ability to grasp and the ability to communicate via the written word.

Soon after birth the baby will demonstrate the first level, which is a grasp reflex. When the palm of his hand is touched, he will curl his fingers around the finger or object with a fair degree of strength. There used to be a custom, and indeed it remains today in some parts of the country, where people visiting a new baby would put money into his hand to see if he would hold it – if he did, then it went into his money box. As the baby

31

is, at this stage, unable to let go once he has grasped anything, most babies would end up with a healthy sum in their box.

The next level, known as vital release, is reached when the baby begins to be able to let go of objects. This is not a deliberate action – which means to say that he cannot let go simply because he chooses to – but is more a protective action. If he should inadvertently get hold of something hot or sharp, the pain felt on the palm of his hand would register on his brain, causing the hand to open and release the object. The same effect can be produced by pinching or pricking the palm of his hand when he is holding a safe object such as a rattle.

Prehensile grasp, the next level of development, is reached when he begins to reach out purposefully and grasp objects. Now it is no longer a reflexive action but a very deliberate one. He sees something he wants, reaches out and grabs it. This involves a movement of the whole hand, the object being held in the palm with the fingers and thumb curled around it, and this limits the baby to being able to pick up only reasonably large objects at this stage. Along with this level comes the ability to release objects voluntarily.

In the next level of development, between six and nine months, the child begins to pick up tiny objects with a pincer-like action. At first it will be a rather clumsy movement, as he more or less rolls the object between his thumb and the side of the forefinger. As he becomes more proficient, so this movement becomes more refined and precise until he is picking up a piece of thread between his thumb and the tip of one of his fingers. This level is known as cortical opposition. Initially, the child will again be able to perform this function with only one hand at a time, then he will reach a point where he is able to pick up something small such as a raisin with one hand and still hang on to it while he picks up another one with the other hand. The next development is achieved when he is able to pick up two such objects, one with each hand, at precisely the same moment.

Once the child can effectively use both hands at the same time he starts to make progress towards the next level of development, which is the ability to perform bimanual functions. These activities will initially involve the child using both hands in a similar fashion at the same time, such as banging a drum with both hands, or clapping two plastic blocks together. If he attempts to put two things together such as Lego bricks or two halves of a barrel, the child will begin by moving the two objects towards each other. Similarly, to take them apart he will pull each one with equal force. As he progresses through this level, however, he will become able to use one hand in a leading role while the other one takes on a supportive role. This enables him to hold a jar still while he takes the top off, or hold a cup still while he pours water into it from another one. At first he will only be able to cope with lids that he can either flick or pull off, but gradually he will learn how to turn lids that need to be unscrewed, and eventually how to turn them the other way to put them back on. For some time the child may appear to be equally proficient with either hand, switching from one to the other for the leading role. Towards the end of this level, however, one hand will be emerging as the dominant one and will be used consistently in preference to the other one.

The last level to be reached in the development of hand function is the ability to write. Everybody is familiar with the sight of a young child sitting with a pencil and piece of paper, filling the page with lines and squiggles and announcing that he is writing. Eventually these scribbles will begin to take on recognisable forms, beginning with shapes, then letters and finally words. Once he has mastered this, the child has another means of expression at his disposal.

The interaction of the six areas

Until now, each area has been discussed individually, but of course as the child grows he is developing in all six areas at the same time. Progress in any one area assists the development of all the other five.

You may have noticed that there are some similarities in the order in which all six areas develop. For instance, in the first level of each area the word *reflex* is mentioned. This is because at the moment of birth the baby is functioning at a purely reflex level. His eyes react to light, he jumps at hearing a loud noise, he reacts to being touched, his limbs move aimlessly, he cries, and he grips hard – but he is not consciously aware of these actions.

He then moves into what is broadly called the vital level. This could also be termed the protective level, because although the baby cannot yet perform any activities at will, he has the ability to protect himself if he is threatened in any way. If something approaches his eyes he is aware enough of it to be able to blink; he is able to register fear at a loud noise, such as a dog barking, and can so summon help; he is able to feel pain, and can react accordingly if he is accidently pinched during nappy changing; he is able to wriggle across the floor and so can to some degree move out of the way of danger; he can cry loud and long if hurt or in distress and so inform mum that something is wrong; and he can instantly let go of something that his hand happens to close on that could be painful. Both of these lower levels of development are largely controlled by the pons and medulla – the lower levels of the brain.

The mid-brain is mostly responsible for the next level of development, which is generally known as the meaningful or purposeful level. Now everything the baby sees, hears and feels begins to take on some meaning. He is able to recognise his mum, and will be amused if she pulls a funny face; he can tell from the sound of her voice whether she is pleased or angry, and can recognise favourite toys by the sound they make; he is able to tell the difference between pain and light touch, and so knows when he is being tickled and can respond accordingly; he has a very efficient means of transportation, so that having seen or heard a favourite person or object across the room he can scuttle off on hands and knees to reach it; he can express vocally his like or dislike of certain activities and so, to some degree, determine whether or not they are repeated; and lastly, having reached the toy he saw from across the room he is able to reach out and pick it up. The baby at this level is beginning to show a sense of purpose – he is doing things because he wants to do them.

All the succeeding levels of development from here on are controlled by the cortex, the outer layer of grey matter of the brain, and if grouped together can be referred to as the thinking levels. As the child begins to understand one or two words of speech, so he is able to speak them – although he will for a long time understand more than he is actually able to say – and so forms the basis of communication. As his understanding of words he hears expands, so will his spoken vocabulary. When the baby first learns to walk, his eyes are also beginning to come together or converge so that he is able to judge distances and see the depth of steps so that he will stop rather than fall down them. As his convergence becomes more firmly established, so he is able to move with greater speed and confidence until he is able to run. He is able to feel the edges of objects that would otherwise appear flat, and so is able to pick up tiny objects with his newly acquired cortical opposition. As his ability to understand what he feels with his hands improves, so his proficiency in hand function improves accordingly. Once he can recognise objects by touch, he is able to reach into a box, quickly identify the object he is looking for, and put it to use. As he begins to understand more complex words and sentence structure, he is also learning to read and write, so that we have a child who can communicate with the world through both the spoken and the written word. As he learns to recognise different coins and their value, so he is able to reach into his pocket and pull out the amount he needs. He is developing powers of reason and judgement, and has the physical ability and agility to experiment and work things out for himself.

Having stated that all areas develop together, it is important that you understand that there is often some discrepancy. Depending on the type of stimulation and opportunity given to the child, he is likely to go slightly ahead in one area and lag behind a little in another. Everyone is familiar with the situation where one baby in the family walks before the expected time but seems to take forever to talk, whereas another baby of similar age in the same family may have a vocabulary of several words but is unable to take a step by himself. In the end, the situation usually evens out. The first baby will suddenly start to chatter non-stop but may, for a time, cease to be interested in climbing and experimenting, while the second one will suddenly find his feet, appearing to be no sooner walking than he is up and down stairs or climbing onto chairs, but at the same time his vocabulary will remain static for a while. In this way, a couple of months' time will again see both children functioning at the same level. In the normally developing child, all areas are forging ahead, although there will be many stops and starts in each area. It is only when one or two areas fall behind the others and stay behind for some considerable time that there is cause for concern.

Chapter 3

So how does this apply to my brain-injured child?

If you are typical of the majority of parents we see, you will over the years have fallen into the pattern of seeing your child as being abnormal in many ways. He is not like other children, he does not do things that other children do. In fact his development has not been normal. It has been our experience that not only are parents not told anything to the contrary of this belief, they are often actively encouraged to hold to it. How many of you have been told, 'Don't expect him to develop in the normal way,' or 'He isn't like other children,' or 'You will have to make allowances for his abnormalities'? It is small wonder that, when faced with these attitudes, the prospects for the future for both your child and yourselves look bleak. We have no doubt at all that some of you have, in your darkest moments, entertained the thought, however briefly, that this child to whom you have given life can barely be called a member of the human race, and could even be termed a freak. Indeed, we do not have to look far back in history to recall times when all such children would have been regarded in such a way. Happily, we have moved a considerable distance in our thinking since then, but we still have a long way to go.

The problem appears to be that people have tended to view a brain-injured child in a very negative way. The emphasis is always placed on what he cannot do rather than what he can. If he cannot see, then he has abnormal vision and is classed as blind. If he does not hear, then he has abnormal hearing and is deaf. If he hears but does not understand, then he is backward, retarded or subnormal, depending on age. If he does not walk, then his movements are abnormal, and so on. We propose that the solution lies in completely reversing the situation, to see the child in a positive light. Instead of looking at what he cannot do, let us see what he can do – what abilities do we have to work with? Instead of regarding your child's various functions as abnormal, we must consider in what ways his development has followed the normal pattern – and then stopped. It is for this reason that it is vital that you are familiar with the development of all areas of function.

We are now going to look at some of your children's 'abnormalities' and compare them with the normal development outlined in the previous chapter. In order to give you as clear a picture as possible, we are using examples which are fictitious to the degree that we did not have a specific child in mind when we wrote them. However, the problems are all ones with which we are familiar. You will note that in each case we speak only of one specific problem. Again, this is purely to illustrate the point. It is a very rare child who has a problem in only one area – usually they exhibit a conglomeration of problems of varying degree in each area of development. I must point out that, sadly although, everything you will read here is true of a child whose problems are due to brain injury, it does not apply where the problem is caused by an external factor: for example, where blindness is due to a physical defect of the eye or deafness is due to blockages within the structure of the ears.

Julie

Julie is six years old and is blind. That is to say, she does not appear to recognise anything or anybody. To evoke any kind of response from her you have to speak to her or touch her, otherwise she does not seem to know that you are there. Her parents have noticed that when she is out in bright sunlight her pupils go smaller and that when she is in a darkened room she seems to look towards the fire or the television. She has also once or twice been seen to blink when her baby brother has waved his hands dangerously near to her face, but this has not happened often enough for them to be sure of its meaning. She does, however, seem strangely fascinated by her mother's red dress.

Now, if we look back to the development of vision, we can trace Julie's progress to date. We know that she has a light reflex, by the fact that her pupils go smaller when she is in bright sunlight, which has exactly the same effect as shining a light into a new baby's eyes. This means that light and dark registers on her brain. She would also appear to have some outline perception which is shown by the fact that she is attracted by a light source in a darkened room, whether it be the fire or TV screen, and is obviously aware of the colour red. She has also been able to protect her eyes from the danger of the baby's poking fingers. However, it is clear that she is not yet able to see any detail, as she still needs strong clues either through sound or touch before she really responds. We have found the block in the development of Julie's vision. You will note that as far as it has gone, the development has been completely normal. The only abnormality lies in the fact that at the age of six, she has not yet moved on to the level of being able to see detail.

Tony

Tony is eight years old. His parents report that apart from a few words he does not appear to understand anything that they say to him. He will always turn around when he hears his name, and responds consistently to the word 'no' regardless of the tone of voice in which it is said. His favourite toy is a ball and nine times out of ten when asked where his ball is, he will trot off to find it. Occasionally he will appear at the table when his mum calls 'dinner' but she is not sure whether he has understood what she has said or has just heard the general sounds associated with the serving of a meal. Tony's parents are sure that he is not deaf because he responds to many sounds around him. He appears from nowhere at the rustle of a sweet paper, but disappears from sight when he hears the preparation for a bath. He is terrified if a police car passes him with sirens blaring, but if he is restless at night he can be calmed by the sound of soft music.

Again, let us look at Tony's pattern of development and compare it with that discussed in the last chapter. It is obvious that the presence of sound registers on his brain, and from his reaction to the siren we can see that he responds to threatening sounds. He is able to discriminate between different sounds he hears and reacts consistently to three or four words. This shows that he has developed pretty well through the first four levels of development. The level he has not yet reached is understanding two words put together or following simple directions. His parents are reasonably sure that it was some time before he showed a real response to any sound, and it has only been in the last couple of years that they are sure that he understands any words at all. Again,

So how does this apply to my brain-injured child?

Tony's development has followed the normal pattern; the abnormality lies in the fact that it took him eight years to reach the present level, whereas it usually only takes one.

Peter

Peter's problem is somewhat different from the previous two, in that at the age of four his tactile development is roughly at the right level for his age. He is able to find his favourite toys from the bottom of the toy box, and can, when asked, reach into a bag and pull out something round and soft, or something made of wool, or something prickly. The thing about Peter which appears abnormal is that he never cries or shouts out when he falls over or bumps into things. Sometimes he will whimper after a particularly bad fall, but even then there seems to be some delay in his response. His mother is always discovering new bruises on his arms and legs and he once had a nasty burn on his hand from touching the iron. His mother reports that he had always been a model child to take for injections, and that he has never really responded to being tickled. When he is absorbed in the television he is often seen to be scratching his legs quite viciously with his finger nails, and when going to sleep he chews on his thumb to the point that the skin becomes broken and bleeds.

When we compare Peter's development with that of a normal child, we see that instead of developing normally to a certain level and then stopping, he has by-passed certain levels before lower ones were successfully completed. He appears to have fallen far short of achieving the levels of responding to pain and light touch. It is obvious that he does feel some discomfort by the fact that he will whimper after a bad fall, but the fact that it is only a whimper and that there is a delay indicates that he is not feeling pain as we know it. His lack of response to tickling suggests that he also has problems at the next level. However, the fact that he persistently scratches his legs and chews his thumbs shows that he must feel something, otherwise he would not do it. What actually happens is that to achieve the feeling equivalent to that produced by a light touch or a stroke, Peter requires a far more intense degree of stimulation. The sensation he produces from scratching and chewing are to him pleasurable, although to us they would be extremely painful. Again, there is nothing abnormal in Peter's responses other than that they persist at the age of four. Remember that no new baby is consciously aware of either pain or light touch. Peter's abnormality, if he has one, is that incomplete development at these levels has not prevented him from going on to higher levels.

Jackie

Jackie is nine years old and cannot move. That is to say, she cannot purposefully get herself from A to B using any means of transportation. Having said that, she is going through series of movements of one kind or another from morning to night, but they are movements which appear to serve no useful purpose. When she is placed on her tummy with something in front of her to move towards, she lifts up her head and everything seems to move at once. She will keep up the struggle for up to fifteen or twenty minutes until she is crying tears of frustration and exhaustion, but at the end of that time she is not even an inch closer to the object than when she started. If lying on her back or supported in a chair she seems unable to be still for more than two minutes at a time; her arms and legs are continuously in motion. If she reaches out towards a toy, her movements are so jerky and uncontrolled that it has been knocked over long before she could hope to pick it up, and when she is excited or upset Jackie resembles a writhing octopus. She becomes a mass of moving arms and legs, which makes it virtually impossible to hold her in any position. During her nine years of life, her parents have frequently heard such words as cerebral palsied, athetoid, spastic – all of which conjure up horrific thoughts of strange diseases.

Looking at Jackie's development it is obvious that it never really got off the ground. But all the movements described are familiar to those who have handled small babies. Stand by the cot of any new baby who is crying for his feed, and watch those little arms and legs in a frenzy of movement. Pick him up and the only reason that he is easy to hold is that he is small and weighs only a few pounds. Now imagine holding a child going through the same movements but who is over half your height, and weighs over three stone – imagine that, and you have Jackie. Put any small baby on his tummy and watch it lift everything but his tummy from the floor and wildly thrash around. The only difference between him and Jackie is that he does not have the stamina to keep it up for more than a couple of minutes. Once again, we see that all of Jackie's movements are perfectly normal but that they are happening at the wrong time in her life.

Andrew

Andrew is twelve years old but, although he chatters non-stop, his speech is nowhere near the level of other children his age. He generally refers to himself by name or as 'me' and is often heard to say, 'Me wants a drink,' or 'Give it to Andrew.' His vocabulary contains some wonderful words, and he will tell you that he is littler than you and that the person who looks after his Mum's hair is called the cut-hair lady. He tends to get rather confused with tenses, and after being for a ride in the car with his father he reported that they had seen his uncle and that they had 'taked him over'. After some deciphering his mother had realised that they had, in fact, overtaken his uncle's car on the road. As far as he is concerned, the general rule is that past tense means simply putting 'ed' on the end of a word – hence, 'he getted up in the morning', 'eated his breakfast', 'then he readed a book'. Andrew's manner of pronouncing words is also less than perfect. He rides on 'twains' and eats 'wawipops' and has a 'fumb' on each hand.

When tracing Andrew's development we see that everything up to this point has been appropriate. He has a good strong cry, which he can use to express rage, fear, or just plain hurt. He can shout at the top of his voice and can whisper so quietly that you can barely hear him. He can reduce his little sister to tears by scolding her when she spoils a game, and can croon lovingly to his pet budgie. He has an extensive vocabulary and is always ready for a chat. Andrew's 'abnormality' lies in the fact that if you heard him from the next room, you would expect a three- or four-year-old to appear – but, I might add, a perfectly normal one.

Susan

Susan is five years old and sits surrounded by toys that she never plays with. She loves to watch them and is fascinated by the sound they make, but does not attempt to pick them up. It is as if she does not know what her hands are for. If a rattle or fuzzy ball is put into her hand, she will grasp it tightly and wave it around, but she does not attempt to transfer it to the other hand. In fact, she will hang onto it until either she drops it or it is taken from her. If her mother's hair happens to come into contact with the palm of Susan's hand, she will grasp it and tug relentlessly until her mother prises her hand open. Mum has recently discovered that the fast way of doing this is to pinch whichever part of the palm of her hand she can get at. This usually produces a squeal from Suzie, but it serves the purpose of releasing mum's hair fast.

Once again, if we compare Susan's function to that outlined in the last chapter we see that she has successfully achieved the first two levels but has gone no further. The fact that she so readily holds onto toys and hair shows that she has an efficient grasp reflex, and her vital release is demonstrated by the instant response to a pinch on the palm of her hand. What she cannot yet do is release an object voluntarily or reach out and pick it up again once she has dropped it.

Carol

The last child we want to talk about is one whose problems do not really lie in any of the six areas. I have included her because I believe there are many parents driven to distraction by the problem but who do not realise that the same principle that applies to the previous six children also applies to this one. Carol is seven years old; her overwhelming problem is that she is never still for a moment. Her parents have repeatedly been told that she is hyperactive, although this is certainly no news to them – they live with her. To watch Carol is like watching a whirlwind; she seems to bounce from one thing to another. The home is completely bare of any ornaments because she would sweep them off in one movement. Nothing is sacred to her; she is able to climb on any furniture and can balance in the most unlikely places. Her concentration is extremely brief; she cannot settle to anything for more than a few moments. Taking her out is a mammoth task; she needs to be held in a vice-like grip the whole time or she would be off – heedless of any danger. The only way her parents can ensure that any of them get any sleep is to fasten her securely into bed, otherwise she would keep going endlessly. Her parents say that she only goes to sleep because she is physically held still and there is nothing else she can do.

Now many of you after reading about Carol will be

thinking what an abnormal child she is. But if you have normal children of your own, or have had close dealings with them, think again. Is this child not absolutely typical of all babies between the age of one and two years? Is this not the age when parents anxiously watch the clock for a time when the child can reasonably be put to bed, and when most babies go for a sleep in the afternoon to prevent mum from becoming a nervous wreck? This is the age when you wonder where on earth he gets all his energy from, when you seem to be constantly surrounded by toys that he spends a couple of minutes with before moving on to something different. If your room was not bare of ornaments, you certainly made sure that they were high enough to be out of his reach. Remember that Carol is seven years old, and her reach is considerably greater than that of a two-year-old. When your child was eighteen months old, the chances are that he was sleeping in a cot. Can you imagine how he would have been if sleeping in a bed? You would almost certainly have needed some form of restrainer on him. So once again, we see that when it occurs at the right age, Carol's behaviour is not so abnormal after all.

We hope by now we have managed to get across the message that in most cases *there is nothing abnormal about your child's function other than that it is happening at the wrong age*. Nobody looks twice at a small baby throwing a temper tantrum, but you just watch the crowds gather if an eight-year-old does the same thing in the street or a crowded store. If you have understood this point, then you should be now looking at your child through different eyes. If this is the case then your next question should automatically be 'So what do we do to get him on the next level?'

In the next chapter, we have taken each of these examples in turn and outlined the kind of treatment we would recommend to solve the problems.

Chapter 4

How do we set about solving these problems?

How can brain injury be treated?

When it comes to the treatment of brain injury, we can sum up what we believe to be essential in two words – *stimulation* and opportunity. We all use only a small percentage of our brain throughout our life. It therefore follows that a very large percentage of our total number of brain cells will not be used, that is to say they remain dormant. It is this large number of dormant cells upon which we rely, and which are in effect the key to our method of treatment.

Over the years, many people have mistakenly believed that we at the Kerland Clinic aim to 'cure' damaged brain cells, to regenerate dead cells, or even to create new ones. It is vitally important that you understand that in no way can this ever happen. Once a brain cell has died it is destroyed forever. Once a brain cell is damaged it will remain damaged, except in a case where it is simply bruised, from which it may well recover. Furthermore, we are all born with our total number of brain cells, and the body is incapable of producing new ones. From the time of birth onwards we are all constantly losing brain cells in varying numbers through many different causes, whether it be high temperature, blows to the head, a brief lack of oxygen, in later years drinking alcohol, or simply with the advent of old age. None of these cells will ever be replaced, but in the majority of cases we manage to continue to function without them. Let us take a moment to consider why this should be so.

Each area of function is controlled by a different area of the brain. As discussed in Chapter 2, the average human being develops in all areas at a more or less equal rate. This would indicate that the percentage of cells that we actually use must be pretty evenly distributed throughout the brain, otherwise this development would be uneven. For example, if your active cells happened to be just in the areas of visual and auditory competence, you would finish up being able to see and hear extremely well but totally unable to feel, move, speak or use your hands. Similarly, if your active cells were evenly distributed except for the fact that none of them happened to fall in the area of language, you would be totally normal in every way except for the fact that you would not be able to utter a sound. If it is true, therefore, that this functional percentage of the brain is evenly distributed, then it must also be true that the percentage of the brain that is dormant must also be evenly distributed. This would account for the fact, as just stated, that despite losing brain cells from birth onwards, the majority of people manage to continue functioning. This is because there is obviously a far greater chance of injury occurring to cells in the large dormant area than to those in the small functioning area. Also, dormant cells can take on the function of damaged active cells to maintain function.

In the case of the brain-injured person, however, we see a different picture. The number of cells affected is far greater, and a vast number are injured at one instant rather than gradually over the years. This is true whether the cause be cord strangulation at birth, a blow to the head, drowning or inflammation of the brain following a virus or vaccination.

Depending on the cause, the nature of the injury will be one of two kinds – either 'diffuse' or 'focal'.

A *diffuse injury* is one in which dead or damaged cells appear throughout the brain – in other words the injury is 'spread out'. This is by far the most common type of injury amongst children we see, and most of the causes already mentioned will result in this. For instance, if the baby is born with the cord around its neck, the tightening cord will cause many blood vessels in the brain to burst. It is highly unlikely that this will be restricted to one area of the brain. A child who falls into a swimming pool suffers a lack of oxygen – which means that the supply to the whole of his brain, not just part, is temporarily cut off. The child who lands on his head after being hit by a car is more likely to involve a reasonably large surface area of his brain than a tiny patch. An inflammation following a virus or vaccination is rarely selective as to which areas of the brain to attack.

A *focal injury* is one in which the dead or damaged cells are confined to a very small area of the brain. Such an injury could be achieved by a single blow to the head with a sharp-pointed instrument such as a pick-axe. If more than one blow were exerted, the resulting injury would most probably diffuse, since it would be virtually impossible to land on exactly the same spot more often than once. It is for this reason that we do not see many children with a focal injury.

You will now be wondering how you can recognise the type of injury your child has suffered. The answer to this is relatively simple. If the injury is spread throughout the brain, there will be a corresponding lack of function, or impaired function, throughout the areas of devopment – that is to say, the child will have visible problems in several areas. These problems may vary in degree – meaning that the child may have very little ability in one area but be only marginally behind in another – but nevertheless a thorough evaluation will reveal incomplete development in several areas. In the event of a focal injury, however, the child will have major problems in only one area of development. This may result in an eight-year-old who can read, write, understand complex instructions, hold an intelligible conversation, but who has to be carried or wheeled from place to place because he has no mobility. Obviously there may be some secondary problems. For instance, a child who has no visual ability will be unable to write words simply because he has never seen a written word. However, if he is of school age, he should be beginning to read braille, a skill which involves a high degree of manual dexterity, proving that his inability to write is a result of his blindness rather than a problem in the area of hand function.

It is important to realise that, if a child or adult has received a focal injury, there is a chance that every cell related to a particular function has been wiped out – including all the dormant cells in that area – and that there is little hope of regaining function in that area. However, with a diffuse injury the damaged cells are spread throughout the brain, and it is a reasonable assumption that there must also be many undamaged cells throughout the brain. As long as there are dormant cells in an area of development, we stand a reasonable chance of acquiring or regaining function.

Having spent some time discussing cells that are dead or damaged, we would now like to state that once we have established the child's problems we no longer concern ourselves with these cells. We are, however, very much concerned with the healthy, dormant cells. We believe that it is possible to bring these cells into action to take over the work of the injured ones. By activating them we can create new pathways to and from the brain that will by-pass the blockage and allow the child to continue his development.

All of our treatment is based on the theories of *neurological organisation* pioneered in the USA by Temple Fay, Evan Thomas, Glenn Doman and Edward Lewinn. While there is as yet no concrete proof to susbtantiate these theories, neither have they been disproved, and the results we have seen with our children lead us to support them wholeheartedly. We will not pretend to expand these theories or the principles behind the treatment, as that would require far more space than is available in this book, but for those of you who would like to study this aspect in more depth there is a recommended reading list at the back of the book. All parents or partners who decide to undertake the programme on a full time basis with our guidance will automatically be taught much about this subject during their child's or partner's initial evaluation.

In very simple terms, the concept of neurological organisation says that the role of the human brain is to relate man to his environment. In order to do this the brain must develop in a very structured and orderly fashion, as described in Chapter 2. A certain amount of stimulation is required in order to attain each level of development, and successful completion of one level leads to the beginning of the next, together with the need for a new stimulus. As this process takes place, the brain matures by virtue of the pathways being used. For example, a baby is born with a light reflex, showing that his visual pathway is open and that the presence of light is registering on the brain. He will now need many exposures to light and dark, providing his eyes with the opportunity to react, so that messages are constantly being sent to the brain via the visual pathway. It is important to state that although there is an average rate of development, this is by no means static, and indeed can be changed in either direction simply by changing the environment. If the new baby is put into a room which is constantly changing from light to dark, then he will undoubtedly reach the level of outline perception before the average infant. However, if that same baby was kept in a darkened room with very infrequent exposure to light, it would be some considerable time before he would begin to see outlines. In other words, regardless of the passing time, the brain is unable to move into higher levels of development until it has received sufficient stimulation at the lower levels. The brain must be taught how something feels before it is able to take over the function.

In the case of the average child, the environment provides enough stimulation to allow all the pathways to mature and development to take place. Obviously, the time span will vary according to the fullness of the environment, and this in itself may vary within one household. For instance, a child born into a family that happens to live in a reasonably dark and gloomy house but which at the same time is very noisy, with doors banging and children shouting, will develop and mature his auditory pathways to the brain faster than the visual pathways, with the result that the area of the brain controlling hearing will be more developed than that controlling sight. This is for no other reason than that his auditory pathway has received far more stimulation than the visual one.

In the case of the brain-injured child, however, the injury acts as a barrier between him and his environment, preventing the normal development from taking place. The barrier prevents the brain from receiving the correct information from the environment. This could mean that a brilliant light shone into the child's eyes may be distorted and received by the brain as a dim flicker, insufficient to cause any reaction. It is at this point that we must intervene if the child is going to develop further.

Our treatment is aimed at the cause of the problem – the brain itself. If we have accepted the fact that the problems suffered by the child or adult are a result of an injury to the brain, it would be senseless to begin to treat eyes, ears or limbs. If you were suffering from severe food poisoning, the symptoms of which were vomiting and an itchy rash, would you be satisfied if the doctor gave you something to stop you being sick and cream for the rash, but did not attempt to give you anything to remove the poison from your system? How effective would the treatment be? Blindness and spasticity are as much the symptoms of brain injury as vomiting and a rash are the symptoms of food poisoning, and therefore the same principles of treatment should apply.

The Kerland method

Our method of treatment is based purely and simply on providing the necessary stimulation together with appropriate opportunity for the child to by-pass the barrier in development. In order to ascertain the form of stimulus required, we must first of all establish the level the child has reached and where he has encountered problems. For problems occurring in the 'input', or sensory, areas (vision, hearing and so on) we will then stimulate the level successfully completed and provide opportunity for the next level, bearing in mind that the normal stimuli of the environment have not been sufficient to accomplish this, on the grounds that, as previously stated, the message received by the brain was being distorted by the injury. If we are to ensure that the correct information reaches the brain we must significantly increase the degree of stimulation. We do this in three different ways. First of all we increase the frequency. If, for instance, an average baby needed fifty exposures to light before he developed a good light reflex, we may need to provide fifty thousand exposures in order to make this happen. Secondly we increase the intensity of the stimulus. If the light from a pen torch is sufficient to cross the visual pathway to the brain of an average infant, we may need to use a 250 watt bulb for the same message to reach an injured brain. Finally, we increase the duration. If continuous daily stimulation of the light reflex were necessary for one week in order for an average baby to gain outline perception, then we may need to keep this up every day for twenty weeks or more to reach the same level with a brain-injured child. Therefore, the three key words to remember with regard to stimulation are *frequency, intensity,* and *duration.* However, this in itself will not be effective if it is not accompanied by the provision of opportunity for the next level. No amount of stimulation of the light reflex will result in outline perception if the child is not presented with outlines to see.

For problems concerning the 'output' or motor areas (such as hand function) we will provide unlimited opportunities for the child to perform the functions he can do successfully together with those he is striving for, but at the same time we will use one of the input pathways to send information to the brain of how the action feels. As already stated, the child cannot perform a function until the brain knows how it feels. An example of this might be a child whose movement in terms of crawling, walking and running is very uncoordinated. It would not be enough simply to allow him the time to practise these functions, because by now his brain has been programmed with the fact that movement is jerky and uncontrolled. This is reinforced every time the child moves. In order to overcome this we must, several times during the day, move the child's limbs for him in a smooth, controlled, coordinated way called *patterning.* The technique of patterning was pioneered by the Institutes for the Achievement of Human Potential in Philadelphia, USA. The purpose of patterning is not to exercise the child's limbs but to programme the damaged brain with the knowledge of how it feels to creep, crawl and walk. If the brain does not know how one of these acts feels, then it is not possible to carry it out. *Patterners* are the parents and volunteers who help the child follow a patterning programme. *Trunkal patterning* is based on the baby's first movement of curling up and straightening out again. *Cross-patterning* requires several patterners, or helpers, as it involves moving the child's left arm and right leg forward, followed by the right arm and left leg. Both these types of patterning are described in detail in Jackie's story on pages 60–64. Other patterns, such as the *roll pattern*, will be self-explanatory as you read through the case studies. We do not go into any of our techniques in detail beause they need to be carried out under close supervision. As soon as the session is completed, the child will be encouraged to perform one of the mobility functions so that his brain may have the opportunity to reproduce the movements that have just been fed in.

Many brain-damaged children have breathing problems. We use a method of breathing patterning that involves a specially designed mask. The technique of *masking*, like that of patterning, was developed by the Institutes for the Achievement of Human Potential. We believe that this technique will not only help to improve the child's breathing but will also reduce his problems with respiratory illness. The mask is a polythene bag, designed to fit over the nose and mouth, with a small valve to allow in a limited amount of oxygen. It was first developed and used on polio patients whose breathing was poor. The mask is used for varying periods, but the initial masking time is for one minute. We describe in Chapter 10 how this technique improves intake of oxygen. Like all our techniques, masking can be dangerous in inexperienced hands and it must *never* be used in any way on your own child without proper training by us.

This chapter opened with the statement that the two factors essential for development are 'stimulation' and 'opportunity'. To summarise briefly, the stimulation is directed to the brain via the sensory pathways in a very structured and organised manner. The child is then put into a situation which provides opportunities for him to use the information received by the brain in order to develop further motor abilities.

We are now going to look again at each of the children described in the last chapter, and give an idea of how we would set about solving their particular problems. Again, we are taking each problem in isolation.

Julie

We have established that Julie has reached the second level of visual development and that she is able to see outlines. The next level she needs to reach is that of seeing details. As already stated, we approach this by stimulating the lower levels with increased frequency, intensity and duration, and providing maximum opportunities for the next level. In Julie's case, we know that she has a good light reflex, and that every time her pupils react a message reaches her brain, albeit a garbled one. We will therefore turn this into a means of treatment. We will increase the frequency by shining lights into her eyes up to 200 or more times each day. We will increase the intensity by making the contrast as sharp as possible, for instance, a 250 watt bulb in a totally black room. We will increase the duration by repeating this day after day after day. We know that she can see outlines, so 20 or 30 times a day we will move a light slowly backwards and forwards in front of her face, and show her large silhouettes. We will surround her with objects designed to catch her visual attention, such as flickering lights and shiny mobiles that will reflect the light.

After doing this for a while, we include more detail in the things we show to Julie. Instead of showing her the outline of a ball, we may make it red with white spots on. The silhouette of a teddy bear will be replaced by a simple picture showing eyes, nose etc. The important factor is the degree of contrast: edges should be exaggerated so that the subject stands out clearly from the background. To increase this contrast, we may for a while use fluorescent paints and show the pictures with an ultra-violet light. This virtually removes distraction and clutter from the environment and allows the child to concentrate her attention on the one thing we want her to see. Each time she is shown a picture, Julie's mother will tell her what it is, using the same word each time. As it becomes obvious that she is finding it easier to see them, we will gradually reduce the use of the special paint and lights. By now, Julie should be becoming quite visually aware, looking at things that move and maybe even smiling when she sees a particular picture. Her mother must now give her the opportunity to use her new ability by approaching her without touching her or making a sound and simply waiting there until Julie looks. She will make faces at her, and hold the cup some distance from her face until she opens her mouth and reaches out. The pictures she shows Julie will gradually reduce in size and contain more and more detail. She will also show her words, written in large red letters, that Julie can relate to, such as the names of her family, the pictures she has been shown, or the parts of her body. The original aim of these words will be to provide more visual stimulation to mature the visual pathways, but as her vision improves it will be our intention that she learns to read. Our aim for Julie will be that she develops from being blind to being able to read sentences and books.

Tony

Tony's problem is that although the spoken word obviously reaches his brain across the auditory pathway, it does not have real meaning to him, with the exception of three words. Why should it be that he manages to understand three particular words when the rest of the English language remains a mystery to him? When you stop to think about it, you can pretty well guarantee that he hears these words every day of his life. His mother will always call his name when trying to get his attention. Whenever he reaches out to something he should not touch he undoubtedly hears the word 'no' and this is probably often accompanied by the object being moved or him being brought away, reinforcing the fact that he must not touch it. And since the ball is the toy he most often plays with, he must hear countless references to it during his day.

The answer to how Tony has learned to understand these three words provides the key to the treatment he needs. The first step is that we must feed words and their meaning into Tony's brain across the auditory pathway in a structured and organised way. During the course of the day, his mother will repeatedly show him sets of pictures, whilst at the same time naming the object he is looking at. These pictures will be organised into categories, basic at first but later becoming more specific. To begin with, he may see a group of animals, a group of household items, or a group of things to eat. Once he has learned the difference between a dog and a cat, he will go on to recognise different breeds of dog. He will see the cards for very brief sessions, literally just as long as it takes to say the name, but he will see them many times during the day and will continue to see them for several days until he knows them. It is this repetition that is the secret to teaching him to understand language.

At the same time as building Tony's vocabulary we will begin to teach him to follow simple directions. At the moment, if you were to tell Tony to sit down, there would be no response. Invariably his mother will say the words out of habit, then some time later, when she notices that he is still wandering around, she will lead him to a chair and gently push him down into it. Unfortunately, she does not generally repeat the words 'sit down' and as it is some minutes since he heard the words there is no association for Tony. It will now be part of his daily routine for his mother to do this with him on several occasions, saying 'sit down' as she gives him a gentle push into the chair. Occasionally she will simply say the words and give him the opportunity to perform the action himself. If he does not, however, she must be certain to carry it through to completion. She will also do this with other simple commands, such as placing an object in front of him and saying 'pick it up' whilst guiding his hands through the motions. The trap that most people fall into is that they say the words but do not follow through with the action. If the child cannot understand the words, how will he ever learn if the words are not accompanied by a demonstration? We could say 'sit down' to you a thousand times a day for the next ten years, but if we never indicated a chair or went through the actions with you, you would not have a chance of successfully following the directions.

Once Tony has learned to follow several individual commands, we will begin to put them together. For instance, instead of saying 'pick it up' and waiting until he has successfully done so before saying 'give it to me', we will now say 'pick it up and give it to me', working on the same principle of helping him to complete the action if he gets stuck. From here on it is a question of making the sentences and directions more complex.

Peter

Peter's problem, as you may remember, is that he by-passed the lower levels in the area of tactile development. In order to fill the gaps we must supply large amounts of stimulation to those levels.

From now on, Peter's day will always begin with a warm bath, in which he is washed with a rough sponge or loofah.

Following the bath he will be sprayed alternately with warm and cold water, and will end the session by being dried with a rough towel, preferably one which has been dried in the open air. This will ensure that he starts each day with his skin fresh and receptive to stimulation.

For the rest of the day at regular intervals Peter's arms and legs will be covered alternately with hot and cold face cloths. He will be brushed from head to toe with a nylon pan scrubber, used in a circular motion on his skin. His mother will repeatedly carry out a sequence of deep pressure massage followed by scratching, pinching and finally lightly stroking the whole surface area of his skin, telling him what she is doing at each stage. At other times she will stroke his skin with a selection of different materials such as velvet, fur, bristles and carpet, again identifying them as she does so. All this will be continued through the stage when Peter is irritated by it to the point where he is actually uncomfortable and finally finds it painful.

By the time we have finished, we would expect Peter to be able to tell whether he is being pinched, scratched, tickled or stroked, and to be able to pinpoint the exact location of the stimulus with his eyes closed. We would also expect him to be able to tell us whether he is being stroked with velvet, silk or fur. We will know that we have succeeded when he bumps himself and lets out an almighty yell.

Jackie

It is not difficult to decide what we are aiming for with Jackie – we simply want mobility for her. As stated in the last chapter, Jackie's movements are all terribly uncontrolled. Therefore, the first thing we must do is to provide her brain with the information that movement *can* be smooth and controlled. In order to do this we will use her tactile pathways to send messages to the brain by carrying out various patterns of movement with Jackie. One of these patterns, the trunkal pattern, involves the baby's first basic movement of curling up and straightening out again, a movement which Jackie is not able to carry out. As you have read several times before, the brain cannot perform a function until it knows how it feels. Several times during the day, Jackie will be placed on her back on the floor with one adult kneeling at her head and one at her feet. These two people will then proceed to work in perfect timing together for the next five minutes. The person at the feet will grasp Jackie around the calves and bend her legs until her knees almost touch her chest. At the same time, the person at the head, who has one hand around each of her wrists, will bring her arms down by her sides until her hands are touching her bottom. As soon as this 'curled up' position has been achieved, they will straighten her out again, the person at the feet pulling her legs down and straightening her knees, and the one at the head extending her arms fully above her head. These two movements will be repeated in a very smooth and rhythmical manner for the full session. It is vitally important that they are not carried out in jerky and uncoordinated fashion or all we will achieve is reprogramming Jackie brain with the fact that it has already established, that all movement is jerky and uncoordinated.

As well as doing this pattern with Jackie we will also begin to give her brain information about higher levels of movement. All the levels of mobility, from commando crawling to running, culminate in a cross-pattern – that is to say, the opposite arm and leg move forward at the same time. We will therefore once again use Jackie's tactile pathways to tell her brain how this movement feels. This pattern will involve three, four or five people, depending on Jackie's size. She will be placed face down on a specially made table with a smooth padded surface, and her head and limbs will be moved by the adults around her. As her head is turned to the left, her left arm is brought forward so that her hand is placed on the table in front of her face, and her right leg is brought up so that a 90° angle is formed at both her hip and her knee. At the same time, her right arm is brought down straight by her side, to end with her hand resting lightly on her bottom, and her left leg is straightened with her toes turned inwards. Her head is then turned to the right, and the position of her limbs is reversed. Again these movements must be carried out in a smooth and controlled manner, and as more people are involved in this pattern it is often suggested that one person counts or they all sing in order to maintain the steady beat that is required. As with the trunkal pattern, cross-patterning is carried out for five minutes at a time.

It would, however, be a complete waste of time doing all of these movements with Jackie if we did not provide her with ample opportunity to use the information that was being put into her brain. Her parents will be instructed to build a wooden ramp, at least eight feet long and two to three feet wide, the height of which is adjustable. Immediately following each session of patterning Jackie will be placed face down at the top of the ramp. The height will have been adjusted to a position where if she lies reasonably still she does not move at all, but if she moves an arm or leg she slides forward a little. The purposes of the ramp is to show Jackie that purposeful movement of her limbs results in forward movement. Gravity is used to her advantage in that she does not need the strength of movement that would be necessary to move her body forward on a flat surface. As her movements become more controlled and coordinated, the angle of the ramp will be gradually reduced until Jackie is able to commando crawl on a flat surface. To help speed this process along, every spare moment that Jackie has will be spent face down on a smooth surface so that she has unlimited opportunity to move. If she shows a tendency to roll onto her back, a device will be made to prevent her from doing so, since she cannot possibly learn how to crawl in that position.

Once Jackie is able to crawl on her tummy, the next stage to aim for is crawling on her hands and knees. At this point the ramp will be replaced by a straddle box, which is of similar proportions but is flat and has a raised padded section down the centre. Jackie will be placed at one end of the box on her tummy, astride this centre piece with one arm and leg on either side of it. There will be about an inch clearance between her tummy and the surface, so that it does not support her weight but it prevents her from lowering herself to be flat on the ground. The sides of the box will be to her shoulder height to prevent her from falling over sideways. Jackie will then be encouraged to move along to the other end of the box. This will be repeated many times during the day and eventually it is hoped that when she reaches the end she will keep on crawling straight out of it.

When we are ready to get Jackie onto her feet, we will make use of an overhead ladder. The rungs will be six inches apart and the ladder will be at a height where, when her feet are on the ground and she is gripping the rung immediately above her, Jackie's arms, legs and body are completely straight. The ladder must be adjustable in height to ensure that this position may be maintained despite any growth that may occur. Jackie will be helped to work her way along the ladder by grasping each rung in turn until she is able to walk from one end to the other without assistance. Once she can do this, we will begin to increase the number of lengths she does each day until she reaches a thousands trips per day. She will then continue to do this each day until she is walking independently *without* the ladder.

At various stages along the way as Jackie's mobility develops, we may add some techniques to help her improve her balance, such as rocking from side to side and head to toe while in the prone position, and spinning both upright and upside down.

Andrew

Andrew's problem concerns the output of language in an organised manner. It follows, therefore, that the first thing we must do is to use input pathways to provide his brain with clear correct information about language. In Andrew's case we are fortunate in the sense that we have two such pathways open to us – the auditory pathway and the visual pathway. This means that we have the opportunity to feed language into his brain in two ways at once, in the first instance by the spoken word and in the second by the written word.

To begin with, we will build up his vocabulary in exactly the same way as with Tony, by using pictures along with the written words, but we will include verbs or 'doing words', adjectives and adverbs or 'descriptive' words and pronouns or 'personal' words.

Secondly, Andrew's family must make sure that they always use correct sentence structure when they speak to him. For instance, it is very hard for him to understand that he should not say 'give it to Andrew' when he hears his mother say 'give it to mummy'. They should try to always let him hear his garbled sentence in its correct form, but in a positive and not negative way. To make this more clear, a negative way of doing this would be to reply to his comment that mummy had been to the cut-hair lady by saying, 'No, Andrew, that's not right, she went to the hairdresser'. If Andrew were constantly corrected in this manner, it is possible that he would eventually decide that the easiest way to avoid being told he had said something wrong was not to say anything. A more positive approach would be simply to say, 'That's right Andrew, mummy went to the hairdresser's'. This could be reinforced by showing a picture of a hairdresser at work together with the written word. Similarly, when he relates his morning's activities to his mum she should reply, 'That's right, you got up, ate your breakfast, then read your book'. When handled in this way, Andrew is given the opportunity to hear the sentence in its correct form but does not have his natural desire to talk stifled in any way.

Finally, correct sentence structure will be reinforced for Andrew by means of the written sentence. His mother will print many sentences for him, including definitions of nouns such as 'a hairdresser is somebody who cuts people's hair', descriptions of people and objects such as 'the hairdresser used scissors to cut mummy's hair' and a diary of things that Andrew does, such as 'on Tuesday morning I went to the hairdresser's with mummy'. In many instances groups of these sentences can be combined with pictures to make a book. It is easy to see how the three sentences already mentioned could be included in a book entitled *The hairdresser*. Every time Andrew reads such a book or hears it read to him, his brain is being provided with language in its correct form, which will eventually be reflected in his speech.

Susan

As already mentioned, Susan does not appear to know what her hands are for. This would suggest that as well as not using them to pick up objects, she is not using them to feel objects and explore surfaces. This in turn would suggest that she has probably not received sufficient tactile stimulation for her sensation to have developed fully. We should therefore begin by sending information to her brain about her hands via her tactile pathway.

Susan's mother will provide general stimulation by means of hot and cold water, massaging, stroking, and so on. In addition to this, several times a day she will sit with her in a position where Susan cannot see her hands. She will then let her feel various objects and textures, manipulating her hands around them and verbally describing what she is feeling in great detail before she is allowed to see it.

Susan is not able to release objects from choice, but we know that she does have the ability to let go when her hand is pinched. It has already been said that one of the functions necessary for a child to reach a new level of development is successful completion of the level before. Therefore, to help her develop the ability to pick up objects purposefully, we need to improve her ability to release. Again, several times a day her mother will put something into her hand for her to grasp, then will pinch the palm of her hand causing her to let go. Every time this happens her brain will be told how it feels to release an object until eventually she is able to do it at will.

Along with all this stimulation, Susan must be given the opportunity to pick up. The only way she will be persuaded to make the effort to do this is if it is something she desperately wants and she knows that nobody else will pick it up for her. For instance, if she has a favourite toy that when shaken makes a particular noise that she especially enjoys, she will not be tempted to attempt to produce this noise if she knows that every time somebody wants to amuse her they shake the toy. It should instead be placed within reach of her but remain silent to the degree that everyone who moves it takes great care not to shake it. If Susan wants to hear the sound, she must do something about it herself. Similarly, when she is hungry a piece of bread or cheese or some other goody should be placed on the tray in front of her but no attempt should be made to feed her. To begin with they should be a reasonable size enabling her to use her whole hand, reducing in size only as Susan develops some ability.

Carol

It is obvious that part of Carol's problem is that she never stays with one activity or object long enough to gain any information from it. Everything she does is at breakneck speed, therefore one of the first things we must do is slow her down. Carol's biggest asset in terms of hyperactivity is her mobility, the fact that she is able to move from object to object and climb to things out of reach. The step in slowing is to remove this form of activity, to take her off her feet. It would not be enough, however, to keep Carol off her feet by simply strapping her into a chair – as soon as you released her she would be as hyperactive as ever. We would use a simple harness that enables her to crawl on her hands and knees, sit, or commando crawl on her tummy, but does not enable her to stand up.

Carol's problem stems not so much from an inability to do things as from general disorganisation. However, the way in which she goes about things prevents her from learning, and so may result in an inability to perform. From our experience, it would appear that organised learning and behaviour start to take place when the baby starts crawling around the floor. This is the time when everything starts to come together and he begins to learn through all his senses at the same time rather than individually. The chances are that Carol, along with most hyperactive children, was a very early walker, and in fact spent very little time moving around the floor. We would therefore recommend that her parents ensure that she spends up to five or six hours each day crawling and commando crawling around the house.

As pointed out, Carol's hyperactivity has prevented her

from learning about her environment. She will automatically be slowed down simply by being prevented from walking and running. We will take this opportunity of presenting her with information through her eyes, ears and hands of everything she comes into contact with in a very organised way.

Many parents fear that by taking their child off their feet, they will cause the child to forget how to walk and run. Invariably, when a hyperactive child who has received this treatment is allowed on his feet again, his ability in this area is improved by the fact that he now does everything with much more control and purpose.

As in the last chapter, with each of these children we have dealt with one problem in isolation. However, we rarely see a child who has only one problem. It may seem a relatively simple matter, from what you have just read, to decide what to do with a child who cannot walk or a child who cannot see, but what if the child can neither walk nor see? Which problem has the greater priority in terms of treatment? How would you fit in patterning plus the overhead ladder plus flashing lights? Which pattern should you use? And just supposing the child also cannot use his hands and does not understand anything? The questions are endless.

This book is aimed at two groups of people. For those of you who are looking for ideas as to what you can do to help your child or partner to supplement the treatment he is already receiving, it is not intended to answer those questions. It is intended only to give ideas of what you might do by giving examples. For those of you who wish to undertake a programme with your child under our guidance, those questions will be answered individually once we have given your child or partner a complete evaluation. We would then take on the role of deciding priorities and teaching you a programme specifically designed for your child or partner.

However, anyone considering this course should be fully aware that it is not easy, and a programme designed by us could involve a child's total waking hours, depending on the extent of his problems. On the other hand, we are sure that by now you have lived with your child and his problems for long enough to have realised that for such a difficult problem there cannot be an easy answer.

Chapter 5

But my child is a mess

Having read the last two chapters, many of you are probably now thinking that it is all very well talking about children with only one problem, but your child has got so many problems that you would not know where to start. In other words, he is a mess.

With that in mind I am now going to tell you about some of our children – real live children, children with names, whose parents have given their permission for us to tell you about them. All of these families have been working at home with their children for at least a year at the time of writing. Some have made remarkable achievements, others still have a long way to go. The children have not been specially selected in any way other than having been with us for at least a year. In some cases I have also included comments from the parents.

Tracy

Tracy lives in Blackpool and was first brought to us when she was fourteen months old. At that time she was very much like a beautiful, fragile, floppy doll. She would occasionally give a little half-smile, but she was generally unresponsive to speech and seemed unaware of whether she was being held by strangers or people she knew. She had no head control at all – her head would flop heavily backwards and forwards – and when put down on the floor she made no attempt to move her limbs, although periodically she would go into a spasm which caused her little body to twist. She was difficult to feed and made very little sound but perhaps the saddest thing of all about Tracy was the fact that she was totally undemanding in every way. There would be no complaint from her if she missed meals, was left to lie in a wet nappy or was totally ignored all day.

Tracy's initial programme consisted of a sequence of activities lasting for half an hour which was to be repeated six times each day. To begin with she would be masked for one minute then she would have a trunkal pattern for three minutes, which would teach her the first basic movements of curling up and stretching out. The next activity was a roll pattern for two minutes, which gives the movements required for rolling over from back to front, then she would be masked again. She would then be shown pictures – very specific pictures all relating to each other – and be told precisely what they were before being swung between two people in three different directions, head to toe, upside down and side to side, each for a minute. She would then hang for a minute from a bar above her head, her hands being held securely in place by an adult, after which she would be masked again. The sequence of trunkal pattern and roll pattern would then be repeated, followed by another mask, and she would then be cross-patterned on the table for five minutes. There would be another mask, and the sequence would end by Tracy being put on the ramp to experiment with moving. If she got to the bottom in less than five minutes she would be given a big cuddle and put back on again.

Within a short time of Tracy and her family returning

home we received a letter from her father, from which I would like to quote the following paragraph:

'Tracy is very well. We are now on our second full week of programme and we have fifty patterners. The response has been fantastic and everyone has taken Tracy to their hearts. She is their little girl and if enthusiasm plays its part we will undoubtedly get the right results. Tracy is eating more and has put on some weight; she does however demand more attention and is no longer content to sit and do nothing. I think we have disturbed a hornet's nest.'

We saw Tracy for her second assessment four and a half months later, and what a different baby we saw. She was now eighteen months old, and not only did she understand many words of speech, she was able to follow several simple commands and knew some parts of her body by name. She recognised the pictures she had been shown and was babbling to adults. In physical terms she had a lot more strength in her limbs and was beginning to move more purposefully, and her head was not flopping so heavily. She would demand attention and liked to watch other children – in fact, Tracy had come to life. It was now time to change her programme. The sequence of activities would still last for thirty minutes and would still be repeated six times each day, but some of the previous activities had been dropped and new ones had replaced them. The sequence would still begin with a mask but then Tracy would have five minutes of a technique known as hip unlocking which was aimed at reducing the tightness that was apparent in her hips. (It had been suggested to her parents that she would eventually need surgery to correct this, but hopefully this exercise would prevent that from becoming necessary.) After another mask, she would see more pictures and then do the same three-minute swing sequence as before, but this time it would be followed by two minutes of sit-ups, where Tracy would be pulled by her hands to a sitting position and would then have to raise her own head until it was in line with her body. It would then be another mask after which she would be shown some written words, then she would kneel holding onto a bar above her head for two minutes. She would then be put onto her hands and knees for three minutes and encouraged to support herself and balance before being masked again and cross-patterned. After the next mask, instead of going on the ramp, Tracy would now do five minutes of assisted crawling on her tummy with somebody behind her blocking her feet to give her something to push against.

Following this assessment, Tracy's father sent us a contribution for our quarterly newsletter which is sent to all our families, and again I would like to quote an extract from it:

'It is just six months since our initial assessment visit to Taunton. Tracy, before then, was a little rag doll who did not have much of a future as far as the enjoyment of her life was concerned.

Tracy's programme was devised and after much blood, sweat and tears on the part of my wife, the patterners were all ready to start. All 60 of them are as enthusiastic now as they were when they began.

We are no longer the sad parents of six or seven months ago. We have a determined little girl who will doubtless one day be able to personally stick one in the eye of all those who said that our efforts were futile and would have little or no effect on Tracy. A political note upon which to end maybe, but I am sure that this echoes the thoughts of others and at least I feel better for having expressed it.'

(Following this inclusion we had an endless stream of phone calls and letters from parents saying that this put into words all that they felt.)

Four months later Tracy's mum phoned to say that she thought Tracy was ready for a change of programme so we went along to see her. Our assessment showed that Tracy was now able to recognise written words (before her second birthday) and was understanding much more. She enjoyed listening to stories and would kick up a fuss if she could not have things her older brother had. Her hips were much looser and she had twice moved forward on the floor without assistance. She was able to support herself on her hands and knees, was trying to use her hands purposefully and was making new sounds. Her mum was right, she needed a new programme.

Still keeping to the half hour of activities six times per day Tracy's sequence would now be quite different. Beginning with a mask she would then sit cross-legged for four minutes in front of a mirror with only slight support at the hips. She would be responsible for holding her head in position, having to lift it if it should flop forward or backward. She would then be swung upside down for a minute before her next mask which would be followed by written words and five minutes of hip unlocking. After the next mask Tracy would spend five minutes on the straddle box to learn about moving forward on all fours, then it would be another mask and a cross pattern. After the last mask she would again do five minutes of assisted crawling, but this time the help would be given from the front, raising her head to keep her shoulders clear of the floor, since Tracy now had enough strength in her legs to push herself.

As I write, Tracy is due for another assessment and we are looking forward to hearing what changes she has made this time. There is one thing that we have been told already, though – at just turned two years old Tracy no longer wears nappies during the day. Her mother is amazed – she was convinced that her daughter would be in nappies until she was at least five.

Alison

Alison is from West Wittering, near Chichester, and her age when we first saw her was three years and five months. Although her comprehension was good, Alison's speech was very poor. She was able to say a number of single words but could not put words together, and most of what she did say was understood only by her immediate family. She could cruise around furniture but could not take any independent steps and she got around by bunny hopping on all fours. She would walk if her hands were held but tended to be on her toes and to take very large, very high steps. She also had some problems with her hands in that although she was able to do most things for her age she was very clumsy.

Like Tracy's, Alison's initial programme consisted of six half-hour sessions per day. She would begin with a mask, then would be shown some written words before being cross-patterned for five minutes. After the next mask she would be made to commando crawl on her tummy for five minutes, and since Alison was very loath to do this we would achieve it by sending her through a crawl box. (This is a long low tunnel, the height of which would allow her to move forward but not to turn over or get up onto all fours. The top of the tunnel is formed by wooden dowels so that it is not dark – and so that if she came to a standstill she could be given a prod!) She would then be masked again before four minutes of spatial activities, consisting of arm and leg swings, swinging from her feet and hanging by her hands from a bar. After the next mask she would have another five minutes of cross-patterning before the final mask and five minutes of walking using the overhead ladder.

Alison's second assessment was five months later and

during that time she had learned to read several words and her comprehension had risen above her age level. She could count to ten, she was conversing more and was putting three words of speech together. She was able to stand by herself for two or three minutes and had in fact taken three or four independent steps. She was walking very well with just one hand and was able to crawl properly on her hands and knees instead of bunny hopping. Her control of her hands had improved considerably which meant that feeding was easier and she was able to build bricks without knocking them down and to thread beads. She had also virtually stopped dribbling.

Her father commented to us that Alison's physical strength had increased by at least 100 per cent and Alison herself was eager to show us how she could hang from the overhead bar with only one hand. She was also, in fact, able to turn a somersault between her arms while hanging from the bar.

We made several changes in Alison's programme. She would now only do five sessions each day; the last half-hour would be spent walking outdoors holding somebody's hand. She would now do only one cross-pattern in each session but would spend five minutes crawling on her hands and knees. Crawling at other times in the day was to be discouraged – we wanted her on her feet. Instead of the swings she would now be spun upside down from a hook in the ceiling by straps around her ankles, and she would be taught to read sentences.

Four months later Alison had another assessment since by then she had made considerable progress and was obviously ready for a change of programme. She was now aged four years and two months and was already able to read sentences. She was able to take twenty-one unassisted steps and her balance had improved to the point where she could now stop, start and steady herself. She was much more vocal and her mother commented that more people outside the family were able to understand her. She was starting to ask questions and would actually initiate conversation with people. She had started attending a local playschool – for normal children – and was mixing well. The biggest change of all was that Alison now wanted to be on her feet – she would get up and walk because she wanted to.

As well as all the things she had achieved by way of progress, Alison had done something else that totally amazed us. Her parents had been so delighted with the changes they had seen in her that they had decided to let Alison do something to help other children with similar problems. So, before her fourth birthday, Alison had done a sponsored swim – and she actually managed to do eight lengths of the pool. People were so overwhelmed to see this tiny brain-damaged girl setting out to help other children that they willingly agreed to sponsor her, and the event raised a staggering £1300. How many three-year-olds – with or without handicaps – do you know who have such an accomplishment behind them? For once in her life Alison had done something that the vast majority of healthy children have not done.

Again it was necessary to make several changes in her programme. She would still do five sessions per day with the sixth half-hour spent walking outside. She would still start with a mask, cross-pattern and mask, then she would hang from the bar for a minute before spinning upside down for four. After the next mask she would practise writing for a minute, then she would swing along the overhead ladder which had now been raised so that her feet did not touch the floor. She would then spin for three minutes sitting in a swing before the next mask and reading sentences, then she would walk for five minutes holding onto ropes which had been suspended from the ladder. After the last mask she would spend three minutes walking by herself, then

77

she would finish up by running with an adult holding each hand.

Shortly after this Alison reached a plateau. She would consistently take between twenty and thirty steps, and the quality of her walking was getting better and better, but she absolutely refused to go beyond thirty steps. This stage continued for a number of weeks, and it was a very desperate period for her parents, who began to wonder whether their daughter had in fact gone as far as she would be able to go. It would have been very easy to give up at this point, but luckily they had the strength and determination to carry on, and eventually the message came through that Alison was on the move again.

When we saw Alison again six months had elapsed since her last assessment, and we were thrilled to see that she was now taking over a hundred consecutive steps (everyone had stopped counting when she got to one hundred and twenty), she was now walking from room to room in the house, and her balance was much better and more controlled, meaning that she could now change direction without holding onto anything. She was, in fact, a walker. She could completely dress and undress herself, could draw a recognisable house and a man and she could even write her name. She was stringing more words of speech together and her parents had both noticed that she was now playing 'just like a normal child'.

We now decided that the time had come to completely change the approach of Alison's programme. Observing her through the day we noted that her breathing was still very shallow and that when she spoke she sounded very breathless. We felt that it was time to introduce some respiratory patterning to try and slow down the rate of her breathing and at the same time make it deeper. (We are purposefully not going into any detail about this technique since doing this without proper supervision and monitoring could be harmful to any child). Respiratory patterning would be carried out with Alison twice a day for half an hour each time. She would then have four physical sessions during the day, only two of which would now contain cross-patterning, and we introduced jumping, rolling and somersaults to increase the control she had of her own body.

By now Alison was fast approaching her fifth birthday and the question of education was beginning to raise its head. The education authority sent a psychologist to assess her formally and following this the recommendation was made that she should go to a special school. On querying this decision, her parents learned that it was made not on the basis of her still limited mobility and speech as they thought, but more on the expectation that she would be a slow learner. This seemed more than a little unfair to us since she could already read many words and write her name, so we advised her parents to fight the decision. As I write, we have just learned that this week Alison started at a local infants school on a trial basis. She is very fortunate that the school in question has a special unit for children with physical disabilities which she will attend when the rest of the class are doing something she cannot join in with or for anything she needs extra help with. This is a far more satisfactory solution – after all, Alison has overcome so many problems during her short life she at least deserves to be given a chance to prove herself. As her parents say, it is now up to her.

Benjamin

When we first saw Benjamin, who lives in Hull, his age was two years and three months. He was a very mobile little boy – mobile, in fact, to the point of being hyperactive. He tended to run everywhere but his running was very uncoordinated, which meant that he fell frequently. He understood only a few single words of speech, usually accompanied by gestures, and did not consistently respond to his name. He had no words of speech, and although he did babble this was more for his own amusement than as a means of communication. He was not doing a lot constructively with his hands in terms of playing, although he was able to feed himself, but perhaps Ben's biggest problem was his almost total lack of awareness of people. He was unable to relate to either adults or other children and was really quite content in his own little world. His smiles seemed to relate to his own little thoughts rather than in response to being spoken to or played with. He also suffered from minor fits.

As with the other two children already discussed, Ben's programme consisted of six half-hour sessions. Beginning with a mask he would then have five minutes of cross-patterning followed by five minutes of commando crawling through the crawl box, with a mask in between. After the next mask he would then do five minutes of crawling on his hands and knees, since this was something he had done for only a very short time before learning to walk. Since Ben was so active on his feet it was very difficult to keep him down on the floor for five minutes so he was to wear a simple harness which would prevent him from standing but would allow complete freedom of movement on all fours. There would then be another mask after which he would be shown some pictures before swinging hand over hand along the overhead ladder – a technique known as *brachiation*. There would then be three minutes of swings followed by a minute of somersaults, another mask and then five more minutes on his hands and knees.

It was six months before we next saw Ben, and by that time the most notable change in him was the increase in his understanding. From a child who had previously

responded to only a few isolated words he was now able
to follow several commands, consistently responded to his
name and enjoyed nursery rhymes. He was a lot more vocal
and was able to hum several recognisable tunes, and he had
learned to throw a ball, put shapes into the appropriate holes
and was beginning to scribble with a pen. In physical terms,
he was much steadier on his feet, walking and running well
with very few falls, had started climbing, and could balance
on one foot. When asked, he was able to pick out all the
pictures he had been shown and he was completely toilet
trained. The most exciting thing for his parents, though,
was that Ben was now very aware of people and would go
up to them, look straight into their face and smile.

Since things were obviously going very well we did not
make a great deal of change in his programme other than
replacing some of the swings and somersaults with spinning
upside down and introducing reading words. We also cut the
length of his crawling on hands and knees by a minute each
time. The regime that Ben was on was obviously suiting him
very well and we did not want to interfere too much since
he was obviously making daily progress in the two areas of
greatest concern – comprehension and relating to people.
We were especially pleased with the changes in him when
we learned that during the six-month period he had had both
measles and chicken pox, both of which had the potential of
pulling him down again.

Ben's next assessment was again six months later and, as
we had hoped, his progress had continued at the same level.
In terms of comprehension he now knew the parts of his body
by name, he was beginning to follow two-step directions and
he understood enough to respond to promises and bribes. His
ability to relate to people had improved to the point where
he was now able to communicate his needs by physically
taking you to whatever he wanted or by putting your hands
on his buttons to ask you to unfasten his dungarees when

he wanted to go to the toilet – which, incidentally, he now did with no assistance. He was able to concentrate for longer, and was playing more constructively with his toys – and he actually now wanted to join in with other children when they were playing. His physical coordination had improved considerably in that he was now able to jump, turn somersaults and was practically able to ride a trike, and his vocalisation now included specific sounds for certain things.

Again, we were thrilled to see this little boy who had previously been so cut off from the world now starting to make positive contact. However, one area that still caused us all some concern was Benjamin's fits which, although not at all serious, were enough to be a nuisance. We therefore decided to introduce some respiratory patterning to his programme since often fits are the result of poor breathing. While discussing Ben's programme with his parents it was mentioned that they often had to change the order of the activities in order to fit the programme around work schedules. We therefore felt that it would better on this occasion if we gave them the total amounts required of each activity rather than a structured sequence. His new programme would therefore consist of four five-minute cross-patterns, twenty minutes of commando crawling, and half an hour on his hands and knees. He would swing along the ladder for a total of ten minutes, split into short sessions, and would spin upside down for a total of thirty minutes, but for a maximum of five minutes at a time. He would be masked thirty times each day and respiratory patterning would be carried out for a total of one hour in sessions lasting for at least fifteen minutes. Intellectual stimulation, consisting of pictures, reading words and a verse to help develop language, would also take place at regular intervals.

We are hoping that when we see Ben again there will be further changes, and judging from phone calls to his parents we will not be disappointed. To quote his mum, he is now 'a real little smasher'.

Louise

Louise is also from Blackpool, and we first saw her just a few days before her third birthday. We have included Louise for a very specific reason, which is to show you that children with severe physical disabilities and no speech can still be very bright and can have a tremendous capacity for learning – as long as they are given the opportunity. Sadly, it is only too often the case that people are ready to assume that because the child (or adult, for that matter) is unable to speak to them and is also physically handicapped, it must follow that he or she is also mentally retarded. How wrong this assumption can be.

We are going to disregard Louise's physical programme, which in many ways has been similar to Tracy's, and concentrate on the intellectual stimulation she has been given and the progress she has made in that area. We hope that after reading this some of you will look at your children – particularly the very young ones – in a different light.

When we first saw Louise her parents were reasonably sure that she understood a lot of what was said to her but found it difficult to prove. She was able to recognise pictures, picking out the appropriate ones with her eyes, and surprised her parents by showing that she also knew a number of shapes by name.

The first stage of Louise's intellectual stimulation was simply reading words. She would be shown them once during each of her six sessions through the day. There would be five in the set and all five would relate to each other – for instance, five family names, five toys, five things she liked to eat. The words would be printed in large red letters on white card, and the set would be changed each week for four weeks, after which they would go back to the first set again. The most important thing about the words was the fact that they were to be shown to Louise very quickly, for just as long as it took to say the word. If she looked away, the person showing the word was to carry on and not follow her with the card or pause until she looked at it. I think that at this stage her parents were more than a little dubious about whether in fact their little brain-damaged daughter – who after all was not yet three – could actually learn to read.

Before Louise's next assessment was due her mother rang to say that she was having some problems with the reading words – at first Louise had thoroughly enjoyed them, but now she seemed quite bored and apathetic about them. She did, however, brighten up considerably if she saw some new ones. We felt that the reason for this was more than likely that Louise had learned the words and so did not see the point of continuing to look at them. We suggested that her mother should discard all the words she had been using and make some new cards.

Louise's next assessment came five months after we had first seen her. When we came to the point of wanting to test her reading her mum sat anxiously by, not really knowing what to expect. We began by holding up words for Louise to see, but not telling her what they said. We then tested her by saying 'look at the word that says . . .' making sure that the cards were far enough apart that there could be no mistaking the direction of her eyes. We also kept varying the position of the words we were asking for to be certain that Louise was not following a pattern. To her mother's amazement, not only did her daughter proceed to pick out all the correct words but she was also obviously thoroughly enjoying herself. Her mum felt sure that it must be a fluke, that Louise could not possibly be able to read all those words, so we kept on going – and eventually, after we had been through all the cards and Louise had not made a single mistake, she had to admit that her little girl could read. She told us that if she had not seen it with her own eyes she would never have believed it possible.

It was obvious from Louise's reaction that she needed a lot more of this type of stimulation and that she needed intellectually stretching – in fact, her mother was going to have to work hard to keep up with her. This time, instead of just words she would be showing her sentences, numbers and colours – all in the same way as before – and we suggested that this time she should test Louise after a couple of months to see if she knew them so that she would not become bored again.

When we saw Louise again six months later we were eager to see how much she had learned – and she was equally as keen to show us. Using the same method of testing, we discovered that she knew all the colours and numbers – and in fact, besides knowing the numbers she could also add them together. (Her mum had rung a few weeks earlier to say that Louise seemed to recognise all the numbers to one hundred and seemed to be getting bored again. We had suggested that she should try some simple addition). She was also able to read all her sentences, and was able to pick out the correct words when tested on comprehension only – for instance, 'which one of these words is something that you wear on your head' and 'which one do you drink out of' etc. Once again her mother was amazed.

By now it was obvious that Louise was like a little sponge, soaking up just as much information as we could give her. Her enthusiasm was as high as it had been on the previous occasion, and she was visibly upset when the testing session came to an end. Here, at least, was a way in which she could prove to people that she was a very bright little girl and that the fact that she could neither walk nor talk did not mean that she was stupid. Her mum said that the only problem they had was one of keeping up with Louise's ability to learn.

Obviously, now, to capitalise on Louise's love of learning we had to introduce some new challenges. The only mistake we could make at this stage was to go too slowly and so let her lose the enjoyment she currently experienced. With the numbers we now moved on to multiplication and subtraction, and with reading we asked her mum to make sentence cards with a difference. One key word would be left out, and Louise would be asked to select an appropriate word to complete the sentence. Her mum would also make some sets of picture cards which would then be cut in half, so that Louise could pick out the corresponding halves to make a whole picture. This would also be done with words. We would also use picture cards to teach her more sophisticated precise information – breeds of dogs, flags of the world, makes and models of cars. (The possibilities here are literally endless.) In addition to all this she would, of course, continue to learn new single words to constantly increase her reading vocabulary.

When Louise's next assessment came round six months later, we arrived quite confident in the fact that she had learned all that she had been taught – and we were not disappointed. It appeared that the more difficult we made the test the better she responded. Nothing made her more excited than preceding the test with 'This is going to be very hard, I don't know whether you will be able to do it'. We could not catch her out on anything. Our problem came in trying to make the questions difficult enough to be a challenge.

The last batch of suggestions we left for Louise included division, to complete the series of numerical operations, followed by simple fractions, beginning by telling her what half of a number was (it would not take long for her to realise that half was the same as divided by two). With reading, it was now time to move on to simple books, and the easiest way to start was by making them for her. In this way you could ensure that the content was something to interest her while at the same time keeping only one sentence on a page to avoid distraction. She was to learn all the different coins by name, and would later go on to learn their values. Louise's older sister was learning French at school, and we made the suggestion that Louise might like to learn along with her. After all, the earlier in life you learn a foreign language the easier you find it.

Louise is currently due for an assessment, and we have no doubt at all that we will find a little girl who is reading books, starting to come to grips with fractions, and is in the first stages of becoming bilingual – and all before her fifth birthday. What was that about lack of speech and mobility meaning mental retardation?

After having read about these four children, you are now probably thinking that it is all very simple and that if your child resembles one of those described you could easily copy that child's programme and get the same results. We would like to say that you are right, but unfortunately it is not quite so simple or clear cut. First of all, no two children are exactly alike, and although programmes may be very similar it is not often that they are exactly alike either. The main problem comes in knowing precisely when to introduce a new activity – doing it too soon may put the child off and prevent him from cooperating when the time is right, while leaving it too late could mean that you have lost the opportunity completely. Also, while the activities have been described to some degree, it is very difficult to know you are doing them accurately without having been shown how.

Over the years there have always been some people who have taken certain aspects of the treatment and carried them out, discarding the parts which they did not like or felt to be unnecessary. Although some of the children may have improved to a point, they have generally not achieved the results they have been looking for. This does not surprise us in the slightest since it is a combination of all the various types of stimulation at the right time that appears to make the thing work. What does sadden us, though, is that these people generally announce that the treatment as a whole does not work – failing to add that they have only done a certain part of it and adapted it to suit themselves. It is difficult enough to make significant progress with any brain-damaged child, and we never guarantee that we will succeed, but we do know that doing less than the whole programme will not be sufficient to bring about the changes you are hoping for.

Chapter 6

Can you help brain-damaged adults?

Although much of this book refers to our work with children, the same theories and principles of treatment apply to adults who have sustained brain damage, and indeed we have successfully treated adults of various ages. However, in practical terms it is much more difficult to carry out a programme with an adult than with a child for a number of reasons. We therefore tend to be far more selective in deciding who we can help than we are with children.

First of all, the brain damage must be traumatic in nature – that is, acquired later in life as the result of an accident or a stroke, for example – and must have been sustained within the last four or five years. We cannot offer help or even hope to adults who have been brain-damaged since birth or early childhood as there would simply be too much to catch up, too many gaps in their experience of life, and they would be too set in their ways. If the patient is not fully mobile, the longer the time elapsed between the injury and the onset of treatment, the greater is the chance of structural abnormality and deformity, such as contractures or foot drop. It also becomes more difficult to motivate patients to exert themselves physically.

The second factor we look at is the patient's emotional state. If he or she is virtually wiped out intellectually and physically, then obviously it is up to the immediate family to decide what is to be done and to get on with it. If, on the other hand, he is aware of what is going on, and of his disability, it is vital to be sure that he himself is motivated to improve his situation. It is one thing to cajole six-year-olds into crawling, standing or attempting to walk – if all else fails, you can physically impose your will on them – but you try to persuade a 6-foot tall, 15-stone 26-year-old to do those same things if he has decided he does not want to or cannot see the point. It does not matter how desperately his family and friends want to see him walk again; if he himself does not have that drive and determination, it will be a lost cause.

We also look at how much thought the family have given to the implications of carrying out a programme on a long-term basis. Obviously, working with an adult is far more tiring physically because of their size and weight. More space is required, equipment is larger, and the number of people needed to help carry out the programme is greater. This in itself can be extremely difficult as, sadly, a brain-damaged adult does not carry quite the same emotional appeal as a small child, and people are likely to be more wary of becoming involved. They may find it difficult to relate to and communicate with the patient and feel that somehow they are intruding on his privacy. They may also feel embarrassed at having to tell somebody of their own age or older that they must do something when they do not want to, or at having to witness them behaving like a child with tears and tantrums. From observation it appears that the greater the degree of damage the easier it is to recruit help, as though somehow the fact that the person is unable to respond or help himself in any way makes it possible for helpers to forget that he is a grown adult and subconsciously regard him more as a helpless child who needs assistance.

The last factor we must consider when deciding whether

we can help is the family unit itself. We try to look as objectively as possible at the strength of the relationships within that unit. Although the members of the family will have no doubt in their minds that they want to do whatever they can to help, they will most probably not be prepared for the emotional pressure that carrying out a programme with a husband or wife, mother or father can create, or for the reactions provoked in the patient himself. This can range from intense resentment at being pushed to do more than he believes he can do, to a refusal to acknowledge that he has an ongoing problem that requires intervention and help, to complete overdependency on a partner.

This latter reaction caused problems of equal proportion to the original trauma itself for one of our families and almost resulted in the break-up of their marriage. The husband had suffered a major stroke in his early forties, which transformed him from a high-powered business man, responsible for large numbers of staff and clients, to a man declared unsuitable for employment. His pension and insurance meant that he would have no financial worries but this did not compensate for his feelings of frustration and loss of self worth. His stroke had left him with no use of his right hand and stiffness of his right foot and leg, which meant that his walking was painfully slow and very unsteady. He had retained the ability to speak, but his speech was slow and sometimes indistinct, and from time to time he lost track of what he was saying. His wife was fully prepared for the physical effort required, but it turned out that neither she nor we had been prepared for the emotional strain that her husband would create. He gradually relinquished responsibility for himself and relied on her more and more to do things for him, make decisions for him, and even to think for him, despite the fact that his physical abilities were improving all the time. Things came to a head when he complained to us that he was bored, he was stuck in the house, his wife was too busy to go out with him, he couldn't do anything – it developed into a monologue of self-pity. His wife said she was equally fed up with the situation. She was sick and tired of running around after him, his walking was now perfectly good enough for him to go out by himself but he would not, his hand function was good enough for him to get himself a drink or a snack but he always expected her to do it for him, he could have helped with some of the household chores but he wouldn't consider it. She had been quite prepared to spend the rest of her life coping with a disabled husband but not one who was lazy, inconsiderate and sorry for himself, and unless he made an effort she had had enough. At first he tried to laugh it off but gradually he realised how strongly she felt, and between us we worked out a strategy to change the situation before it was too late. He had, in fact, grown to enjoy being disabled, and had to do a lot of adjusting to adopt a positive outlook on life and focus on what he could do rather than what he could not. Happily, they developed new interests, both separately and together, and started to look forward to a future which, although different from the one they had initially planned, still held promise.

Emotional strain of a different nature can occur in a situation where a child or a young adult has to try and come to terms with the fact that their mother or father, who throughout their life has provided direction, support and discipline, now needs to be looked after and told what to do. This is an unnatural situation for them and is likely to make them feel uncomfortable, embarrassed, angry and bereft, for in fact they have lost a parent. In trying to make sense of the situation and some kind of adjustment they are likely inadvertently to cause additional problems for the other parent, who will be experiencing his or her own feelings of bewilderment, anger and loss.

Introducing a programme into such a precarious family unit could either have a settling influence or a disruptive one. Some children will welcome the opportunity to take control, establish some order and routine, and make a positive constructive contribution to their parent's longed-for recovery. Others will resent the fact that not only have they to cope with the effective loss of a parent in the true sense, but are now also expected to adjust to switching roles with that parent, treating them as a child, telling them what to do. Some children are, in fact, totally unable to make this adjustment, being able to cope with it only by pretending that the situation does not exist and reducing their involvement with the parent to an absolute minimum. Trying to force this child to help with a programme would, in all probability, result in eventual alienation from both parents.

What we are saying, then, is that there are obviously occasions where working with an adult can be both beneficial and rewarding, and for this reason every case should be looked at very closely and not dismissed out of hand. However, the potential problems surrounding a brain-damaged adult and their family are far greater and more complex than in the case of a child and should not be minimised in any way. The last thing we want to do is to take an already very difficult situation and turn it into an impossible one. This would serve no useful purpose whatsoever and could prove the difference between a family being able to cope or not.

Chapter 7

Can you help someone in a coma?

Coma is generally defined by the medical profession and lay people alike as a state of unconsciousness from which the patient cannot be aroused. There are varying degrees of coma, ranging from a patient at one end of the scale who is a hair's breadth away from death, to one at the other end who is hovering on the verge of consciousness. However, in practical terms, a comatose patient is one who is able to make no conscious response to any stimulus, and it is highly unlikely that the untrained eye would be able to detect the degree of coma.

Coma can be the result of various problems, including high temperatures, blows to the head, drowning – indeed, any of the causes of brain injury already mentioned can lead to a coma. A person can be in a comatose state for days, months and, in some cases, even years. Some patients make a spontaneous and complete recovery; others will remain in coma until they die. In the case of spontaneous recovery, what appears to happen is that the brain suffers severe bruising, which causes swelling of the cells and tissues preventing the brain from functioning. As this swelling subsides, the brain returns to its normal functional state, and many patients have been known to wake up, sit up and ask for something to eat after having been in a comatose state for days. In other cases, the damage to the brain cells is more extensive than simply bruising and the patient may emerge from the coma more gradually, and show some obvious impairment of function. Finally, as already stated, some patients will not recover, but will stay in a comatose state for the rest of their lives, needing intensive nursing care. Sadly, when a patient goes into a coma, it is invariably impossible to state whether or not they will make a spontaneous recovery unless it has already been determined that there has been extensive damage to the brain. It is fair to state, however, that the longer the person remains in a comatose state, the more unlikely become the chances of a spontaneous recovery.

To summarise, then, people who have suffered a brain injury that results in coma fall into three groups. The first group, those who make a spontaneous and complete recovery, have no need for the information in this book other than for general interest. The second group, those who recover from the coma but suffer impairment of function, whether it be moderate or severe, would then be considered to be brain injured, and as such may find some answers to their particular problems in the other chapters of this book. It is the last group of patients, those who remain in coma and as yet have shown no sign of recovery, with whom this chapter is concerned.

It has already been said that a person in a comatose state is alive but unable to make a conscious response to any stimulus. Indeed, in some cases life may be maintained only with the assistance of support machines. If we are to regain some kind of functional life we must first re-establish the pathways between the environment and the patient's brain. There are five basic senses offering us pathways in to the brain – sight, hearing, touch, taste and smell – and we must utilise all of them to the full.

You will remember from the last chapter that the three key

words were frequency, intensity and duration. These words are of even more importance for the comatose patient, but one of them plays an even bigger part than the other two. Frequency is important in that the person needs regular reminders that there is a world here that he is part of and he must not be allowed long periods of being left in his twilight world. Duration is important in that we must keep up the stimulation relentlessly until some response, however small, is seen. In cases reported where patients have been brought out of coma by relatives and friends talking about familiar things or playing tapes of favourite music, we believe that it was the sheer duration of auditory stimulation that finally broke through the barrier, not so much what was actually being said. It would be interesting to know whether the same results could have been achieved had the patients not received auditory stimulation but instead been given an endless barrage of flashing lights, or had been pinched, scratched or tickled relentlessly. However, the vital word in the treatment of a person in coma is intensity. Remember that his brain is not consciously receiving any messages from the environment. It would therefore be useless to spend hours on end providing stimulation that was equal in intensity only to that in a normal environment, as none of it would be even reaching the source of the problem.

To summarise, then, in order to treat the comatose patient we must bombard all five senses at regular intervals throughout the day with a stimulus of greater intensity than that found in the normal environment, and we must be prepared to keep it up for days on end until a response is achieved. Your next question is, we are sure, how this stimulation is provided.

Those of you who have had the misfortune of being closely involved with a person in coma will no doubt have seen from time to time a doctor or nurse check the patient's reflexes by shining a torch into his eyes, making a loud noise and poking or prodding his limbs or scratching the soles of his feet. It is these very tests on which our treatment of patients in coma is based, the difference being that as a test they are done once only and are repeated on a limited basis throughout the day, whereas when used as a treatment they are repeated several times in succession and the whole procedure is carried out on a very regular basis throughout the day.

Before going on to give more specific details, I must point out that your flexibility with regard to how much of the treatment you are actually able to do will be affected greatly by whether the patient is in hospital or at home in your care. When a person has been in coma for some time, and is not reliant on life support machines and in no immediate danger, the family are sometimes given the option of having him home and nursing him themselves, under the supervision of the doctor and health visitor. If this is the case then obviously you will have greater freedom in how much stimulation you provide. If on the other hand the patient is requiring hospital care, you will have to work very much within the limits of the hospital routine and rely on the co-operation of the staff. If this is the case, then great care must be taken at all times not to interfere with any nursing procedures or to make excessive demands on the staff. We will write on the assumption that the patient is at home with the family but in the knowledge that in the right circumstances all of the points discussed can be carried out equally satisfactorily in hospital, providing that the family are allowed unlimited visiting.

The first point that we would make is that the patient is moved to the noisiest most active part of the building. All too often the comatose patient is kept in a quiet, darkened room, where people whisper and move slowly. This is absolutely the last thing he needs. First of all, it is unnecessary, light and sound are not registering on his brain, so why do you need to keep the sun out of his eyes or to whisper? It is certainly not going to bother the patient! Secondly, and much more important, how is his brain ever going to begin to react to these things again if they are carefully kept from him? If we could pick the ideal spot for him, it would be half in the kitchen and half in the living room, so that he was in the pathway of everyone walking from one to the other, within earshot of pots and pans being bashed about in the kitchen and the television in the living room, and with all the familiar smells coming from the kitchen. This would be even better if there were young people in the house, as then there would be bound to be doors slamming, music blaring, and raised voices. Finally, if I could have complete freedom, I would have him wear as little clothing as was practicable so that he was exposed to a temperature change every time the door opened and closed, and put him in a confined but public space, so that every time somebody passed they were forced to either brush against him or bump into him. In this way, even at the times when it was impossible to give him direct stimulation, his environment would be such that there was a fair chance that he would receive indirect stimulation through each of his senses. Obviously it would be impossible for the majority of people to meet all of those conditions, but we hope that the illustration has shown what we are aiming for.

In terms of direct stimulation, we would begin by bombarding all five senses. By the side of the bed, we would keep the following collection: a 500 watt bulb on an extension lead (if it is impossible to darken the room you may need an outsize carton to place over both your own head and that of the patient to provide the contrasting darkness); a selection of loud noise makers such as two blocks of wood, a football rattle, a compressed air horn and a whistle; a selection of bottles containing strong-tasting substances, such as tabasco sauce, concentrated lemon juice, mustard, strong unsweetened coffee and a selection of bottles containing pungent substances, such as ammonia, vinegar, heavy perfume and petrol. We would then make a point of every fifteen minutes going to his bedside and going through the following routine. The light would be shone into his face ten times in succession for one second each time with a five-second period of darkness between each flash. One of the noise makers would be selected, and he would be exposed to ten short sharp bursts of sound, each followed by a five-second period of silence, again for contrast. (The same sound would be used for the whole session but a different one could be used in the following sessions.) We would then take each limb in turn and systematically poke, prod, pinch and massage, repeating the stimulation over the body area. (It is no use lightly stroking, because remember he cannot feel it.) An alternative to this for some sessions would be to lightly run an ice cube over his skin quickly followed by an extremely hot towel or face cloth. Next we would select one of the smell bottles and waft it two or three times beneath his nose, and finally we would take one of the taste bottles and with an eye dropper deposit a small amount of the substance onto his tongue. The whole routine takes only minutes, but in that time we have stimulated all of his senses.

If at any stage a response to any one of the stimuli is noticed, then that particular one should be repeated as many times as possible. For instance, if pinching the sole of his foot causes him to pull his leg away, then you pinch the sole of his foot a thousand times a day. If blowing the air horn makes him blink his eyes, then you blow the air horn a thousand times. With the comatose patient we are looking for response, therefore anything that evokes a response should be repeated ad nauseam. We are in effect telling him that he is not allowed to slip away from us and giving him something to hang on to. Once we can bring about consistent response in all areas, then we have brought the patient out of his comatose state and can treat him as any other suffering from brain injury.

We believe that in the case of coma the same principles apply to child and adult alike, with the same chances of success (although as stated at the beginning of the book, success can never be guaranteed). In the case of an adult, however, once he is out of the coma we must then establish whether or not there has been any lasting brain injury, and at that point assess the feasibility of embarking on a programme.

Chapter 8

What can I do about my child's fits?

If your child is normal in all aspects except that he suffers fits, then in nearly all cases the label of *epileptic* causes many problems. Many young people are given the impression that they have some terrible disease. It is very important to realise that anyone's brain can, under certain circumstances, produce a fit. It appears, however, that this otherwise normal child has a brain that will do this frequently or infrequently, in many ways. We believe that there is no disgrace in being epileptic and that other complaints such as asthma and migraine are just as problematic.

The clinical manifestations of epilepsy are varied and include such different conditions as:

1 a loss of awareness
2 a loss of muscle control
3 both of the above symptoms with accompanying loss of consciousness.

There are many, many other types (if they can be labelled types) of seizure, fit or convulsion. All of them can be induced in everyone by suitable means and any person can be made to have a convulsion if a suitable electric current is applied to the scalp. It would clearly be wrong to consider such persons as suffering from epilepsy.

The diagnosis of 'epileptic' should be used only if fits occur regularly and do not require provocation, or if a fit can be provoked by something that most people are frequently exposed to in everday life.

There are two types of epileptics:

1 Some adults and children come from families who have a past history of 'epilepsy'. This epileptic tendency seems to pass through some families for many generations, some members developing fits but the vast majority having none at all.

2 Some adults or children labelled epileptic are labelled thus because they have some other medical problem such as brain injury or a tumour which is producing the recurring abnormalities.

An easy way of classifying epilepsy is to say that the fits are of known or unknown origin. However, we believe we can help anyone who suffers from fits and so we tend to disregard the fact of whether their origin is known or unknown. It must be realised that we cannot provide a complete cure, but our programme does, in many cases, bring about a reduction in the number, severity and after-effects of a fit. In some cases they are eradicated completely.

Once you have read that statement, if your child suffers fits we are sure your pulse has quickened. Ours would in the same circumstances. It appears to us that the state and the medical world has its own cure for fits:

1 Drugs to suppress the symptoms.

2 Monetary grants to parents to help provide the child or adult with whatever he needs.

Whilst we feel it is a very good idea to help financially, we reserve the right to disagree that the current medications are the correct treatment for epileptics. They quite simply suppress the symptoms but do nothing to eradicate the cause:

102

What can I do about my child's fits?

Prominal (methylphenobarbiton – a barbiturate)
Epanutin (phenytoin)
Mysoline (primidone)
Tegretol (carbamazepine)
Epilim (sodium valproate)

The above drugs are just some of those which our children are taking, some have been taking them for years having suffered what could only loosely be described as a fit. WHY?

The medical world tells us that these drugs must be taken with absolute regularity and that adequate dosage is essential. No reduction in treatment should be made until there has been a complete freedom from seizures for at least three years. I would like to believe that this willingness to reduce medication is because there is a widespread belief in our theories – which you will by now have realised are based on the fact that we attempt to programme the brain to understand what something feels like. If I suffered many fits, was labelled epileptic, took a course of medication for a minimum of three years and suffered no further signs of a fit and was labelled as 'well', I would be very happy. Unfortunately, this attempt – if it may be so called, to programme the brain, has several major drawbacks.

The one thing on which we wholeheartedly agree is the fact that the sudden cessation of this type of treatment can precipitate 'status epilepticus' – which can be fatal. Many of the medications used are habit-forming and in our experience it can take as long as two or three years to wean a child off these drugs. We must state that in some cases the use of drugs is, in our opinion, the only method of controlling seizures. It is simple and effective, but what of the side effects!

Barbiturates and Mysoline cause drowsiness, Mysoline sometimes causes vomiting and stomach pains.

103

Epanutin in large doses can cause severe gum disorders. Tegretol and similar drugs occasionally cause problems with blood-cell formation.

A combination of these drugs causes symptoms which resemble drunkenness and can disturb the folic acid metabolism.

Many of the children we see have other major problems besides epilepsy, which in most cases stem from their brain injury. Most of them would have been given anti-epileptic drugs which might help alleviate the symptoms of epilepsy but, in our opinion, do absolutely nothing to solve the underlying problem, and into the bargain make the solving of the child's other problems much more difficult.

We understand why these drugs are used and why the current attitudes towards seizures are adopted but we believe that they should lead to further investigation into possible cures and not to treatment which, to you and us, seems to make the problem worse.

It is therefore true to say that we do not agree with the accepted treatment for epilepsy. If your child has ever suffered fits, have you ever been told, either by a doctor or a social worker, something along the following lines?

1 'Your child will have to take drugs for the rest of his life.'
2 'He will have to attend a special school.'
3 'He cannot ever lead a normal life.'
4 'All fits cause more brain damage so the drugs are necessary.'
5 'Don't overstimulate him because this will cause more fits.'
6 'There is no cure for epilepsy.'

We would respectfully disagree with these statements. It is now well established that some individuals with brain injury have recovered functions without treatment. Some people function remarkably well considering the amount of brain tissue they have had removed or damaged. Therefore, in our eyes, the brain must have great recuperative powers. Unless the epilepsy is inherited we feel that to avoid the stigma of being epileptic, mentally retarded, cerebral palsied, and so on, we would prefer to call the child brain-injured. Equally it must be said that our treatment can be just as successful with children or adults who have 'inherited' epilepsy.

With some exceptions, medical opinion long ago tacitly accepted the belief that the most that could be done for brain-injured children was to help them adjust to their handicap (including fits). This belief has led the medical world to treat symptoms rather than the problems behind the symptoms. Having, in our opinion, made this error, the current treatment for fits lacks sound scientific orientation and so fails to be critical of its own methods. Most medical and surgical disciplines have learned to look for the possible harmful effects of medications and techniques and they are accustomed to reporting these when noted. But we have not always found this to be the case regarding the harmful effects of some methods used in the conventional treatment of brain injury and fits.

In treating the crippling symptoms of brain injury and fits, there must always be the danger of putting the brain to rest by reducing the memory intake and immobilising motor functions. Regression of speech, mental functions and mobility have resulted from the current conventional treatment of epilepsy. In some cases conventional methods work but, in our experience, generally they do not. Moreover they frequently compound other existing problems. If there is a silence about the harmful effects of accepted therapy, the mothers of children who appear to have regressed are generally not silent; however, they come across a barrier which they cannot breach. Of course the testimony of these parents would not be accepted as scientific evidence; however, we suggest that it should be listened to.

In presenting our concept of the cause and treatment of seizures, we must state that we are considering the subject of seizures as it relates to children and their brain injury. The important difference between the younger child whose functional development is not yet complete, and the adult is that the child has a large margin of uncompleted maturation and functional development. To the extent that such a margin may exist in individuals beyond this stage it is possible that the same concept may be applicable to them. In practice we generally believe this to be so.

Over the past two hundred years there has been great progress in the exploration of the anatomy and the structural details of the brain and spinal cord, which together compose the central nervous system. In the last seventy years the manner in which these structures work has been intensively studied and many firmly founded facts have been established. Although many neurological phenomena have been discovered and closely examined, the exact way in which these activities, especially those which imitate a seizure, fit into the total picture of brain function remains largely a matter of interpretation and conjecture. Some of the interpretations have ultimately been confirmed, others have stood the test of time but have not been proved – but conversely they have not been disproved. We cannot prove our theories except that in many cases they appear to work, which to us seems a good enough reason to pursue them. To parents they appear to work, in conjunction with other programmes, far more successfully than anything else previously tried.

Our concept proposes that anti-convulsant drugs impair both the cortical control of the reflex mechanisms for seizures and the developmental and maturational process by which such control is ultimately established. We also propose that the injured cerebral cortex may achieve and retain its controlling functional position in the central nervous system. This is achieved by improving maturation and development through a specially structured environment, with sensory inputs of highly increased frequency, intensity and duration under the best possible conditions in each home. Finally we propose that it is probable that conditions which establish such cortical control also decrease the tendency in the damaged brain to generate abnormal electrical discharges which cause seizures.

In English-speaking countries, seizures are generally known as one of the following: epilepsy, convulsions, grand mal, petit mal, jerks, absences, spells, fits, turns, spasms and probably some other names which mean the same. Each country, indeed each language, has coined its own name for seizures. In a similar manner, drug manufacturers devise many different names for the same drug. No matter what the label is for any anti-convulsant, we see the following major disadvantages:

1 They are ineffective.
2 They have disfiguring side effects.
3 They cause insidious and serious alterations in the metabolic processes.
4 They are mind dulling and stupefying.
5 They can cause potential fatal reactions.
6 They may cause incoordination as a further neurological disorder.
7 The use of these drugs violates a basic concept of medicine – whenever possible treat the *cause* and not the *symptom*.

At present, the use of these drugs is not not unlike poisoning the dog that barks at the burglar – in other words relief from the noise was obtained but I lost my priceless collection of stamps. It seems to us that we have reached the point where we treat a patient with a given medication and assume that it is the progression of the disease that makes things worse rather than the 'pill to cure'.

We suggest that the best environment possible must be obtained and that all the unfavourable influences must be eliminated. The favourable influences must be reinforced as outlined in Chapter 10. There is no 'cure-all'; each child or adult will have a neurological organisation programme and a nutritional programme devised specifically for that individual. There may be many similarities, but no two programmes will be identical.

In our view seizure activity is the result of three factors working in conjunction:

1. Injured brain cells, having survived the initial injury, may not yet have fully recovered. This may lead to stress and to a generation of stress signals – this in turn could release the reflex mechanism which will lead to a seizure.
2. A brain that is already unstable because it is injured may have other influences in its environment which will hasten the advent of a fit.
3. The immature neurological organisation and development involving the cortex, the cerebellum and reticular system – in other words the brain – has not matured properly.

We will slowly withdraw the drugs, under medical supervision, and instead have the parents apply our programmes, the aim being to mature the brain. If the seizure activity persists and there is no other influence such as a tumour, or hydrocephalus, a fresh injury or a recurring injury, then this is usually an indication that our programmes have not been designed properly, we do not know enough, or that the correction of environmental factors, such as lack of oxygen, have not been pursued vigorously enough.

To deal with this problem of oxygen insufficiency, which may be crucial to a child's progress and in the control of seizures where they exist, we use various effective measures, which include masking and respiratory patterning, as described in Chapter 10. Increased oxygen availability provided by these two methods has, in our opinion, been the most effective single action taken by us in decreasing seizure activity, together with reducing and eradicating the use of anti-convulsant medications.

If we also advance or improve the rate of neurological growth and thus allow the brain to mature, the cortex should acquire the correct controlling functional position and proper relationships with the cerebellum and the reticular system. This removes or prevents the release of the reflex mechanism which causes seizures. By their action the current anti-convulsant medications used interfere drastically with the achievement of this ideal.

Conclusions

Sadly for many thousands of children who are presently diagnosed as having the non-existent disease of epilepsy and in consequence are taking anti-convulsant drugs, their problems are multiplied instead of eliminated. The true understanding of their problem will take at least several decades. Man has never really understood the process of convulsing, which he has seen as fits, seizures, spells, lunacy, possession by evil spirits or more recently as a disease called epilepsy.

Until recent times mankind, with very few notable exceptions, has seen convulsion disorders as being the possession of the victim by some sort of evil spirit. The cure was drastic: either death or cleansing by fasting. People who suffered convulsions have suffered because onlookers always associated their problem with insanity or feeble-mindedness. This has been undoubtedly true despite the accepted fact that Alexander the Great, Mohammed, Caesar and Napoleon – who by their achievements have been labelled men of exceptional quality – still suffered severe seizures.

We are therefore proposing that 'epilepsy' is not a disease at all but a symptom of brain injury which occurs when insufficient oxygen reaches the brain. We believe that seizures are a mechanism provided by nature to protect the body in a similar way to vomiting, which restores a state of normality. We do not cure seizures but simply attempt to cure the problem which triggers this natural mechanism. Our theory leads us to assume that fits are the product of loss of cortical control of the lower levels of the brain which control basic functions necessary for life. Our answer is to remove the drugs slowly (these drugs reduce cortical control) and then to improve cortical control by a programme aimed at maturing the central nervous system and thus improve the development of the brain.

We try to accomplish this by

1 A practical programme of liquid balance and diet.
2 Achieving greater oxygen availability to the brain by the use of masking and respiratory patterning.
3 Gradual and progressive reduction with the aim of discontinuing the taking of all anti-convulsant medications.
4 Effective programmes of neurological organisation aimed at maturing the brain.

How many times have we wished that the medical world could (or indeed would even try) to understand what we believe to be true. Why do we believe our treatment of seizures to be more effective than any other? Simply because it *works*. Many millions of pounds have been used to explore the use of drugs and other techniques to control seizures. We submit that this is a waste of money, time and resources. How many thousands of children must pay the dreadful penalties that millions have paid in the past as a result of primitive and misguided beliefs concerning the causes and treatment of fits. We will see.

Chapter 9

How do people cope emotionally?

Over the years much has been said by onlookers about the emotional aspect of our methods – that what we do is cruel, distressing for the child, that it upsets parents, it creates emotional strain, it breaks up marriages. The parents themselves, on the other hand, invariably put forward an entirely different point of view. Since our therapy depends heavily on the involvement of people outside the immediate family, it is important that we talk about various aspects of the emotional demands that will be made on all concerned.

First and foremost, it is vital to understand and accept that in the early stages the child is going to complain, often bitterly. This is a perfectly normal reaction, especially when you consider that in most cases the child's life prior to this has been without pressure or demands, he has been generally cocooned, protected and, above all, kept happy. Obviously it will be a great shock to the system when his safe little world is changed to one where he is pushed to do things, the safe haven of mum's arms is replaced by a table or the floor, and the tears which used to produce cuddles and soft voices now have no effect. He has no way whatsoever of even beginning to comprehend that all this is happening because his parents love him dearly and ultimately want a better life than has been predicted for him. In all honesty, except in the case of an older mentally impaired child, we cannot afford to give him a choice. It is therefore imperative that we press on regardless.

It has often been suggested that we should start very slowly, introducing the child to the activities over a period of time, not pushing too hard, stopping if the child becomes upset, and so on. From experience we have learned that this is just about the worst way of going about it for a variety of reasons. If parents are seriously intent on carrying out a programme on an ongoing basis it is vital that they are in control, not the child, and that one way or another it is going to be done. Although initially some of the exercises may feel strange and cause a little discomfort, none of them should actually hurt. Usually the complaints are based on nothing more than the child objecting to being handled or having an adult's will imposed upon him. If at this stage the parents can grit their teeth and carry on, restricting all cuddles and games until the end of the session, invariably within a couple of weeks the protests die down as the child learns that it is going to happen anyway so he might as well save his energy. On the other hand, if every time the child cries the exercises come to a halt and he is picked up or allowed to run away, all he will learn is that if he complains he can make it all stop. When after a time the parents realise they are getting nowhere and resolve to press on regardless, he will simply protest louder and for longer until he achieves the same result. Not only does this approach prolong the agony for the child, but it causes further problems in its own right:

> A sequence of activities which should take half an hour drags on to an hour, hour and a half or even longer, making it impossible to fit in the required number of sessions.

> Helpers become more and more upset by the child's

apparent distress, more and more frustrated at their lack of ability to help constructively and gradually find excuses not to come.

Parents, especially the one at home all day with the child, become tired, intolerant, and begin to disagree about how to handle the situation, sometimes resulting in the decision that it cannot possibly work.

Although the parents are worn out, and most of their lives are being spent trying to carry out the programme, they are not in fact achieving enough to bring about an improvement in the child. They become dispirited, the conclusion reached again being that the programme does not work.

In the middle of all this sits a severely brain-damaged child who has, without his parents realising it, been allowed to decide his own future.

For all these reasons, we strongly advocate that parents adopt the approach of working through all protests, making it clear to the child from the outset that he is not being given the choice of whether it happens or not. Even then, parents can make life more difficult for themselves than it need be by talking the child into crying, by suggesting that he will not like certain exercises, or by telling helpers that he will not do them, or, even worse, by crying with the child.

Having said all of this, we do realise that it is not nearly as easy as it sounds, especially for those most closely involved with the child. It is difficult for any parent to detach themselves emotionally from their crying child, especially one they feel needs extra care and protection. Some parents are so fiercely over-protective of their child that they want to shield him from all unpleasant experience, and sadly in those cases we can do little, if anything, to help. Fortunately most parents are so desperate to improve their child's situation that they are able to overcome these feelings, or at least to shunt them into the background for the time required to do an effective programme. The ones who handle this the most successfully are those who manage to conceal their true emotions from their child, the ones who laugh, tease and cajole their way through it. We do not doubt for a moment that these parents experience just as much heart-wrenching as others, but they have learned the wisdom of shedding their tears and expressing their feelings out of sight of the child. Even the youngest, most severely handicapped child is sensitive to his parents' emotional state, especially his mother's, and if he instinctively feels that she is not happy and at ease with the situation, then neither will he be.

The rest of the family

Now let's look at other members of the family. Brothers and sisters are obviously going to be affected by the family's decision to carry out a programme with their child – but then equally they are going to be affected by simply having a brain-damaged child in the family. The question here is to what extent they are affected, and how a potentially negative situation can be turned into a positive, constructive one. The first thing to remember is that children are basically adaptable and capable of understanding a lot more than we often give them credit for. With the exception of the very young, it is important to sit down and explain to them in simple terms what you are going to do and why, stressing that the whole purpose will be to help make the handicapped child able to do more, which will in turn make it easier for the whole family to enjoy their lives. Their opinion on whether to go ahead should not be sought – they too must understand that you have already made that decision – but they should be encouraged to suggest ways of making it easier to cope with. Many like to be actively involved, and indeed we have seen some superb patterners among the brothers and sisters of our children.

It is vital to parents to make it clear from the outset that the fact that they will be spending a lot of time working with the child does not mean that the other children will be neglected or will have to fight for attention and affection – which is another very good reason for not giving in to the brain-damaged child's protests, resulting in the programme taking all day. Brothers and sisters can cope extremely well with the demands of the programme as long as they know that they are still important and that their parents will still give them periods of undivided attention. Frequently, too, they appreciate the fact that at last the handicapped child is being made to do things he does not want to do and no longer has the ability to control the whole family by crying. Far greater emotional turbulence can be caused by children feeling that their parents employ a completely different set of rules and values for their hurt child than by seeing the family pulling together constructively to help that child fit into their world.

The other members of the family worthy of discussion at this point are grandparents, and in particular those who live close to the family. In our experience they can prove to be either the child's salvation or his downfall. Broadly speaking they fall into two categories: those who can sufficiently detach themselves emotionally from the child to allow an objective view of his problems and his future, and those who can not. However much they may want to, those in the latter group are totally unable to give any practical help because their urge to protect, to give comforting cuddles and join in the tears is too great. Simply being in the same room during programming leads to tension between them and the parents, and the child soon learns to play to Granny's sympathies. We have even seen extreme cases of children

116

turning away from their parents because they keep being told that 'It's all their fault' or 'Mummy's cruel' or 'Granny won't make you do it'. In our view, these grandparents should be restricted to helping only in indirect ways – collecting the other children from school, shopping, ironing – and to spending time playing with the child outside of programme. In this way they can still play a very useful role but will not make the already difficult task of doing a programme more so. On the other hand, those who are able to handle the emotional detachment can prove to be the backbone of the patterning team, taking control when Mum is not there, giving emotional support to the parents and other children, and generally being there when needed. An added bonus is that they often add to the equation their own form of wisdom based on years of experience with children and with life in general. It is, of course, up to each family to decide which role best suits their own parents.

Voluntary help from outside the family

Now let's consider for a moment that group of people who are a vital requirement for any family on programme, the volunteer helpers. In a typical family these helpers will be a mixture of friends, neighbours and total strangers. All are there because they want to do their bit towards giving a child with problems the chance of a better future but often, particularly in the case of strangers, they will be unprepared for what lies in front of them. Those who have not had any previous contact with brain-damaged children will have their own idea of what the child will be like, which will often bear little resemblance to what they are faced with. Unless they are very close friends of the family, the chances are they will have had little or no experience of handling such a child and will not be prepared for varying degrees of stiffness or floppiness, or for the level of helplessness evident in many children. The child will sense their lack of confidence and will either feel insecure, making them miserable, or quickly take advantage of the situation by stiffening up, 'playing dead' or generally making life difficult for the newcomer. Although they have the very best of intentions, some people will be frightened by this and others will be overwhelmed by pity, in both cases being unable to give practical physical help. They can, of course, still have a very useful involvement by organising rotas, preparing flashcards and so on. Some families have even had volunteers offering to do ironing or cooking, leaving them free to work with the child.

Once families have managed to secure some voluntary help there is the ongoing problem of keeping them. The key to this lies in making them feel useful. To start with, their initial feelings of nervousness and caution will lessen if they are actually taught to do the exercises with a large rag doll or a teddy bear with extended limbs (made by stuffing socks with foam and attaching to the existing limbs, thus creating 'joints'). This will have the double benefit of removing the distraction of the child complaining and resisting while they are trying to concentrate on the exercise, and of allowing them to gain confidence before they actually work with the child. This in turn makes the child feel more secure. Some families choose to have a meeting of all interested volunteers and teach them all at the same time; others prefer to bring them in one or two at a time. Whichever way it is done, the point must be made that if they are unable to make a regular ongoing commitment they should not pursue it any further. Those who do stay to become part of the team invariably find that ultimately they gain as much from the experience as they give to the family.

When parents are dependent on volunteer help they are often nervous that they may stop coming, making it difficult or impossible for the family to continue the programme. To many parents it does not come easy to have to ask for help, and they feel that they are imposing on people, which leads them to try and do as much as possible themselves. This is, in fact, counter-productive and is a very easy way of losing volunteers rather than keeping them. This is very understandable if you consider that most of them will be reasonably busy people with other demands on their time, whether it be in the form of work, a young family or a home to run. Despite this they are prepared to give up time on a regular basis because they feel that their help is needed and they can make a positive contribution to a tragic situation. If, however, they then find that on repeated occasions they turn up only to find that for a large portion of the time they are a 'spare part' as mum insists on doing everything herself rather than risk imposing, it will not be long before they start thinking about the pile of washing up they have left in the sink, the meal that needs preparing for the family, or the shopping waiting to be done. If people are going to make time in their already busy lives they need to feel that it is time well spent, and generally speaking they will welcome being fully utilised.

It is an interesting observation that the role of helpers gradually and very subtly changes over a period of time, especially those who were not already friends of the family when they started. To begin with they turn up out of a sense of duty or sympathy or simply gratitude that their own children are healthy, with the feeling of having a job to do. At this point they probably feel that it will be very one-sided in that they will be doing all the giving, but before long they realise that on the contrary they are actually gaining an awful lot from the experience. Patterners have told us that their involvement with a child on programme has radically changed their attitudes and values and they have found it a very humbling experience. Often they become supportive in other ways and lasting friendship develops that will continue for years after the need to help with the programme ceases. One family told us after their first Christmas since starting programme that it was the best they had ever had. They had an 'open house' for their helpers throughout the Christmas period and said it was like having an ongoing party for their child and themselves. This was a dramatic contrast to previous years when their child's problems and their own helplessness had combined to make them feel somewhat left out.

How does the child feel?

Finally, we must give some thought to the emotions of the child himself. As we have already said, it is a foregone conclusion that the child is initially going to be upset when the programme starts, but it is most important to keep this in perspective. It is not, in fact, the actual programme which is upsetting him; it is the fact that his cosy little world is being disturbed. What parents have to try to look at objectively is how much more emotional upset will lie ahead of him if they do not at least try to give him a better quality of life. Although tears may flow in vast quantities, this does not always mean that the child is as upset as he appears. This is simply the best, most effective means of communication he can use to bring about the desired effect – of making everything stop.

There is no doubt that a small handicapped child evokes feeling of sympathy, protectiveness, and emotion, and there are usually plenty of offers from people to hold, cuddle or comfort the child. However, when that same child reaches the age of nine or ten and still has the same problems but without some of the 'appeal' that goes with a baby, those offers become somewhat thin on the ground. If sympathy and cuddles solved the problems of these children there would be no need for organisations such as ours, but sadly they do not. One father told us how he tackled this issue with some of his helpers, and we have found his story useful to pass on to other families. In the early days of his two-year-old son's programme, he had a group of middle-aged helpers who were obviously upset by the little boy's distress and constantly made comments such as 'Poor little thing, it's a shame' and 'It's hurting him' and 'Isn't this cruel'. The father brought everything to a halt, picked his son up and comforted him, then propped him in the corner of an armchair surrounded by cushions. Within minutes he had stopped crying, and the general feeling was 'That's better, he's happy now', at which point the father said to the ladies:

'Fine, if that's how you like to see him, we won't make him work, but in ten years time he'll be a lot bigger and still just sitting there, still not able to see, still not able to move, still not able to do anything for himself – but at least he might be happy. On the other hand, we've got a chance to give him an even happier life by helping him to achieve more, but that might mean that he has to cry for a while. Now which is it going to be?'

The result was that they all took a deep breath, said 'Let's get on with it' and in fact became a very positive team of helpers.

This chapter closes with a viewpoint expressed to us by an adult who had suffered from athetoid cerebral palsy since birth. Despite this he was fully independent with a good job, but still experienced great difficulties in motor control. He told us how he wished there had been something like our programme when he was a child and that his parents had had the foresight to push him through it, which led on to a discussion about whether parents should or should not inflict such a regime on their child. We felt that his opinion would be extremely relevant as he was the only member of the group who could speak from a position of first-hand experience of brain damage, and he was in no doubt whatsoever. He likened being brain-damaged to being trapped in a steel cage, with the only possible way out being for somebody to cut through the bars with an acetylene torch. He said that of course you would be frightened by the flames, you might even get burned a little in the process, and you would beg them to stop, but that both you and your rescuers would know that they must not stop because if they did you would have to stay in that cage for the rest of your life, which was not an acceptable alternative. The depth of feeling with which he spoke removed any lingering vestiges of hesitation that maybe we were being a little too harsh in our approach.

Chapter 10

Creating a healthy environment for the brain

Nutrition

A long as a child is growing, his nutritional requirements remain high. In order to supply all the essential nutrients a large amount of food is required and yet a child's stomach is relatively small. This means that there is no room at all for sweets, biscuits, sweet artificial drinks, cakes or ice creams. This does not mean that brain-injured children cannot be treated like any other child, simply that they need good nutritional food more than well children if they are to survive. We can also safely conclude that you can be fairly sure of raising healthy children by making every effort to be healthy parents.

One of the most important aids we can give you about nutrition is some advice regarding the selection of foods that contain the most needed nutrients. In this country we have for many years produced and imported more food than we need and to keep it from spoiling it is highly processed and refined. However, the process of refining takes away and destroys much of the nutritional value of the original food whilst leaving the calorific value relatively untouched. These foods will not allow for repair or growth of the body, but make for wear and tear – rather than wear and repair.

Recent studies have also shown that the human body under stress requires a substantial increase in its nutritional intake. This is true for well children and doubly so for brain-injured children, who are undergoing physical and emotional stress of a very high nature whilst they are on a programme of neurological organisation. Nutritional research is being carried on at an hitherto unprecedented rate in almost every medical school, university and pharmaceutical laboratory throughout the world.

This vast amount of research deals basically with the forty nutrients which cannot be made in the body and are collectively spoken of as our body requirements. They are essential fatty acids, fifteen vitamins, fourteen minerals and ten amino acids. Healthy people will, in their diet, have an adequate intake of these nutrients. All these nutrients work together, and a lack of any one will result in the body underproducing hundreds of the estimated ten thousand compounds which the body produces, that are essential for the maintenance of good health.

Probably no one nutrient is ever totally lacking in an otherwise adequate diet, but partial, simultaneous deficiencies are common. The missing nutrients which allow illnesses to develop have generally been discarded in the processing and refining of the majority of our foodstuffs.

Nutrition, however, is not concerned with disease; it is basically a study of building and maintaining health. It can hardly be overemphasised that nutrition can never be competitive with the practice of medicine – it is quite simply an aid to health for the patient and the doctor.

Brain-injured children, our subject, generally not only have a poor diet, but are lacking in their daily intake of vitamins. It must be stressed that this is often through no fault of the parents. In our experience, most brain-injured children are given diets which include foodstuffs which an ordinary child would not be consuming. As a result of their brain injury, many of our children do not have an efficient ability to metabolise their food, that is, to receive the most benefit from their food intake.

To meet the nutritional demands of stress must be the first consideration in planning a diet and in coping with any disease. We must, therefore, design individual nutritional programmes for each child. In the same way that it requires more materials for the repair of a damaged car than for the upkeep of one in good condition, every nutrient is needed in larger amounts to repair a body damaged by multiple stresses that cause disease and result from it.

These children are always close to their families and, not being parents of brain-injured children, it would be impossible for us to state the emotional stresses that can, and often do, exist in such families. These stresses are very often transmitted in one way or other to the brain-injured child. The child also suffers stress in many different ways, but they all boil down to an individual child's inability to communicate, to walk, talk, see, hear, eat, drink: in fact, to behave as any normal child. There is also an additional physical stress for the child who suffers continuous infections. The body is unable to cope with this and a vicious circle is created – constant infections lower the child's resistance and this in turn makes the child more prone to pick up more infections, the result being that he never gets the chance to fully recover.

Many of the children are on a wide range of prescribed medications. In our opinion the majority of the drugs prescribed to control the symptoms of brain injury are poisonous to the degree that they are introducing unnatural substances into the system. These drugs can produce dietary deficiencies by destroying nutrients, using them up more quickly than usual, preventing their absorption, increasing their excretion or chemically taking their place.

An increasing amount of suffering could be avoided if

steps were taken to improve nutrition immediately the initial symptoms have been noted. In following this rule the nutritionist must see that each of the forty body requirements is adequately supplied – erring on the side of too much rather than too little. Most medications are effective when used alone, but no nutrient is of value unless accompanied by the thirty-nine others. Obviously, normal children will have some deficiencies but brain-injured children will have larger, multiple deficiencies and in these cases we will design a nutritional programme for each child. A close watch should be kept on the diet and fluid intake and the supplements given to the child as directed. It is also important for brain-injured adults to have a healthy diet. Although their bodies are no longer growing and developing, the nutritional points that we make in this chapter apply equally to adults. In this chapter we will deliberately avoid stating dosages because vitamins in the wrong hands can be just as dangerous as any other medicine.

Vitamins A and D

These vitamins are two of the essential fat-soluble vitamins. Vitamin A has many functions but it is best known for its relationship to vision, especially where a deficiency results in night blindness. 'A' is also very helpful in the growth and repair of body tissues. It helps to maintain the health of the skin, prompts the secretion of gastric juices necessary for proper digestion of proteins and protects all linings of the digestive tract, kidneys, bladder, eyes and lungs.

Vitamin A does not occur in vegetables; however, carotene, which is found primarily in yellow and green foods, is made into vitamin A by the body. One of the richest natural sources of vitamin A is fish liver oil.

Borderline vitamin A deficiencies are believed to be widespread. They arise from either an inadequate intake of the vitamin or an inadequate intake of other nutrients needed for its absorption and utilisation.

A deficiency in vitamin A may show itself in the form of:

poor vision
over-sensitivity
boils, carbuncles
dandruff
eye infections
bad teeth and weak bones
inadequate formation of red and white corpuscles
poor resistance to infection

Vitamin D functions to regulate the amount of calcium and phosporus in the blood. It is sometimes called the sunshine vitamin because sunlight acting on the oils of the skin can produce it and the body absorbs it.

Deficiencies can lead to poor bone development and maintenance. It is especially important to children because, without vitamin D, bones and teeth do not calcify.

B vitamins
The fifteen or more B vitamins are meagrely supplied in our diet as nearly all our refined foodstuffs eliminate most of these vitamins in the processes involved. B complex is a collective group of water-soluble vitamins which rely on the presence of each other in order to fully function. They are called complex because they work together, complement each other and are often found together in natural foodstuffs.

B-complex vitamins are important in providing the body with energy – basically by converting carbohydrates into glucose, which the body 'burns' to produce energy. They are also important in the metabolism of protein and fats and in the functioning of the nervous system. Many nutritionists agree that stressful conditions increase the demand on the body's supply of nutrients, especially those of the B complex and vitamin C. These vitamins are water-soluble and cannot be stored in the body – they must therefore be replenished daily.

There are four good natural sources of the B vitamins – brewers' yeast, liver, wheatgerm and unpolished rice. They appear to be needed equally in every part of the body and thus their overall importance cannot be stated too strongly.

Vitamin C

Of all the vitamins, vitamin C is probably the best known. It is found almost exclusively in foods of plant origin, such as citrus fruits and vegetables. A prolonged lack of vitamin C results in scurvy, whilst lesser insufficiencies may lead to bleeding gums, anaemia and bone and teeth weaknesses in growing children.

Vitamin C also helps with the absorption of iron and has special functions in maintaining white blood cells, which fight infections. It is also important to the body's manufacturing of a substance called collagen, which binds cells together and is necessary for the connective tissue, or fibrous elements, in skin, ligaments and bones as well as for rebuilding tissues during wound healing.

Another important factor is C's ability to protect some of the B vitamins and vitamins A and E from oxidation, when they undergo a chemical reaction with oxygen in the body to form different products. Once again, an adequate supply of this vitamin is essential for good health but it must be remembered that, being water-soluble, it cannot be stored in the body and it must therefore be replenished daily.

Vitamin E

Vitamin E is found in vegetable oils such as olive oil. It is fat-soluble and can be stored in the body. It is an anti-oxidant, which means that it decreases the oxidation of other substances in the body. For example, E prevents A from breaking down and combining with other substances. Vitamin E also plays a role in cellular respiration of all muscles, especially cardiac and skeletal. It is understood to help nourish cells, strengthen capillary walls and protect the red blood cells.

It is known that an adequate supply of vitamin E decreases the body's need for oxygen. As you probably realise, many brain-injured children have breathing problems, so that this vitamin is particularly helpful in this area. Vitamin E is thought to be essential to glandular function and a deficiency decreases the production of all pituitary hormones. From our experience, when vitamin E is not absorbed, i.e. the child is deficient in E, then infections do and will more readily appear. As mentioned previously, all vitamins act and react with each other: for example, the more vitamin E in your diet, the less vitamin A is needed and the more A can be stored.

The amount of vitamin E, as with most other nutrients, needed daily varies widely and some individuals require much more than others. The need for vitamin E is increased by stress and in most cases there is a long deprivation of an adequate intake. This vitamin is discarded with every ounce of flour refined and the average intake of E has decreased drastically in the last 50 years. It is, therefore, very easy to see why, when and how deficiencies of vitamin E occur in the average person. This being the case for you and me, what of the brain-injured child?

Minerals

The individual functions of minerals are well known, but a complex inter-relationship also exists amongst the essential minerals. Numerous acid-forming minerals and alkali-forming minerals interact to maintain the body's acid balance. Minerals function together; some act as catalysts for biological reactions; combinations of minerals help to form the components of body compounds, such as hormones and enzymes.

Although minerals constitute a relatively small part of the total body, they are very important for adequate metabolic functions. About 96 per cent of the body weight is carbohydrate, fat, protein and water. The remaining 4 per cent is made up of as many as sixty minerals. Twenty-one of these have been proved to be essential for correct human nutrition but many of the others may play just as essential a role. The basic problem is that mineral intake can, and often does, fall short of need. Vitamin intake may be satisfactory but problems can be caused by a lack of the right mineral. In some ways, minerals are a lot like vitamins. However, they differ in that they are inorganic chemicals; this means that living organisms cannot create them. In addition the human body does not 'burn' or 'consume' minerals in quite the same way as it does vitamins (which are organic or carbon-containing compounds). However, the basic life processes of individual cells throughout the body require many minerals in a manner similar to vitamins. In fact some vitamins and minerals work together, such as calcium and vitamin D, magnesium and vitamin B6.

Most multi-mineral supplement tablets will contain calcium, phosphorus, iron, copper, iodine, manganese, zinc, magnesium, potassium, and vitamin D, to enable their proper utilisation. Obviously a great deal could be, and has been, written, not only about vitamins but each individual nutrient. We, however, intend to use only calcium as an example of the effect that one mineral deficiency can have.

Calcium
Although 99 per cent of the calcium in the body is in the 238 bones and teeth, symptoms resulting from an undersupply to

the nerves and soft tissues can make life almost unbearable. Calcium helps in the transmission of nerve impulses. When a deficiency occurs, nerves become tense and you become irritable. As the deficiency is maintained or increased the person becomes restless, unable to relax and quick-tempered, which does nothing for the person's popularity. The fatigue experienced also becomes out of proportion to the amount of work done. Such a person will often become an 'air-swallower' and this can lead to all different kinds of indigestions, so that the person involved becomes a constant user of indigestion remedies. These can make the deficiency worse, as they prevent any more calcium from being absorbed. In fact, such a person becomes his own worst enemy. However, all these symptoms can quickly be relieved when an adequate supply of calcium reaches the nerves.

A calcium deficiency often shows itself in insomnia, which is another form of an inability to relax. If blood calcium drops very low, muscles tend to suffer more from cramps or muscle spasms. These symptoms occur in many people, especially as they get older.

A lack of calcium can make adolescents (whose requirements obviously sky-rocket) become so irritable that the most tolerant parent can become exasperated by their behaviour. During the months before a girl's periods start, the level of her blood calcium drops and she exhibits the symptoms as previously described. It is at this time that what was an adequate intake becomes inadequate. A similar situation occurs when periods cease. Her diet, which had previously supplied adequate calcium, is now no longer adequate and calcium deficiency symptoms occur. The calcium intake should, of course, be increased at such times along with vitamin D.

In ancient times calcium was also used as a pain killer but is apparently recommended infrequently for this except by nutritionists.

Obviously most people associate a lack of calcium with a susceptibility to tooth decay and a weak bone structure. This is true, and both calcium and vitamin D must be adequately supplied, absorbed and retained if dental and skeletal health are to be maintained. Numerous American surveys have shown that the deficiency of calcium is more widespread than that of any other nutrient. Milk is our only dependable source. In some countries adequate supplies of calcium can be obtained from mustard and turnip greens, soya beans and blackstrap molasses – who eats any of those in the UK today? Many people in other parts of the world may have other nutrient deficiencies, but are nevertheless receiving an adequate calcium supply. Although they do not drink much milk, many orientals eat soya bean curds, and the Eskimos, African natives and the American Indians all receive adequate supplies of calcium from the bones of fish and the small game which formed a large part of their diet. In most so-called civilised countries the calcium needs of a person who does not drink milk can only be met by a calcium supplement. Many of the people who live in a civilised world do have an adequate diet, but it involves excessive amounts of phosphorus. The calcium and phosphorus combine in the stomach and we have, once again, the beginning of a calcium deficiency. Liver and yeast, which contain many other essential nutrients, are also very high in phosphorus but low in calcium. If large quantities of these foods are consumed, either a large amount of milk or a calcium supplement should be taken.

It is very important to realise the interdependency of all the various essential nutrients and that an excess or deficiency of one can be equally damaging. Deficiencies need to be made up and a proper balance maintained thereafter. The effects of drugs on each other and the side effects of drugs on the system are often acknowledged but we rarely stop to think about the ways that medication may be interfering with nutrition. Drugs have saved, and will continue to save, millions of lives. A great deal has been said and written about vitamin C, but for over thirty years it has been known that this vitamin is a detoxifying agent. The amount of vitamin C in the bloodstream falls dramatically when drugs are taken.

Household remedies such as aspirin and other painkillers, if taken regularly, can produce deficiencies in vitamin C for a person who previously had an adequate diet.

Brain-injured children tend to suffer more than most in respect of nutritional deficiencies and it is an essential part of their programme that these deficiencies or excesses be put right in order to create a personally healthy environment for the child.

Most of the children who are submitted to a neurological organisation programme will, for the first time in their lives, undergo high stress and be exposed to many new things. They will, therefore, need nutritional supplements to their otherwise adequate diet because we hope to promote growth throughout the body. A nutritional diet with supplements will therefore be a major part of the child's programme.

Nearly all of our children will also be taking some sort of medication prescribed by their doctor. It will be one of our aims to remove this medication gradually, under medical supervision. A careful medication reduction programme will also be part of the child's programme. This does not mean that we do not believe that drugs can play an important part in maintaining life: they can. But as we know from bitter experience many of our children are regular drug addicts and consume large quantities of barbiturates or anti-convulsants. In one case we had a child on programme who early in his life had suffered three minor epileptic fits but at the age of five years was still consuming five different drugs and had, in four years, taken over eight different anti-convulsants or barbiturates. It is true that these drugs will help to control the symptoms but they do nothing to remove the cause of the symptoms.

The symptoms of brain injury and such afflictions as spina bifida and hydrocephalus appear to be more prolific in Great Britain than most other countries of the world. This can be explained very easily:

1 An efficient health service identifies more cases than an inefficient one.
2 Population censuses mean that accurate statistics are available.

Let us take the area of South Wales, from the Rhondda Valley to Llanelli. There is the highest percentage of spina bifida children in Great Britain in this area. There is also a high incidence of brain injury. It is possible that some of these cases are caused genetically, by the continued and accepted inbreeding between a declining population for a hundred years.

Now you ask, 'What has this to do with my brain-injured child?' It is our contention that some children are born brain-injured quite simply because of the area the parents lived in for the years prior to conception or even possibly for the nine months during which mum carried the child.

Interesting factors:

1 Local diets – what do they contain? Perhaps excessive or deficient amounts of minerals or vitamin.
2 Local housing and content of water, e.g. lead pipes, blue asbestos padding.
3 Adequate diets becoming inadequate when processed foods replace natural home-grown produce.

Some of these problems could be avoided by potential mums and dads taking vitamins and mineral supplements. Such techniques as hair analysis could enable us to determine a deficiency or excess of all minerals – healthy parents are more likely to have healthy babies, allowing for the usual risks at birth. Not only must it be our aim to provide our brain-injured children with adequate diet but we must also try and educate the rest of the family to eat an adequate diet.

Providing an adequate oxygen supply

In order to create a healthy environment for the brain, a very important fact has emerged. We believe the problems of breathing in a brain-injured child to be of great significance. We all breathe – that is an accepted fact – or we die. The process of dying through not breathing is as follows (over a five-minute period):

1 The person will not be able to co-ordinate his movements well.
2 He will experience series of petit mal seizures – very much like those experienced by many brain-injured children.
3 He will then become completely unable to co-ordinate and unable to hold anything in his hands.
4 A seizure very similar to a grand mal seizure will then occur.
5 When sufficient brain cells are dead, the person will die.

The natural conclusion to the above synopsis is that if breathing is so important to you and me – supposedly 'well' human beings – then it is much more important to brain-injured children, who may already have lost many functioning brain cells from the area which controls respiratory function. The child's breathing might just develop so far and no further. Is this because he has suffered the death of many brain cells which should have been activated at a certain point in development as the child's capabilities expand or because there was no need for the child to breathe in an improved fashion, that is, because of the original brain injury?

We do not yet know the answer, but it is obvious to us that if we improve the chest capacity and breathing of the brain-injured child, we will also improve the amount of oxygen getting to his already damaged brain (assuming that oxygen transport is normal). Historically, breathing problems have been one of the largest single problems of brain-injured children. Breathing problems are also the most common form of death in these children.

We have two ways of increasing the oxygen supply to the brain: one involves increasing the capacity of breathing, while the other involves the regulation of the pattern of breathing.

Masking
The technique used to increase the capacity of breathing is that of *masking*, which we have mentioned several times already in the case studies. In order to understand how the mask works, it is necessary to understand how the human body regulates its oxygen supply. If a human being breathes air that does not contain enough oxygen to sustain life, that person will breathe faster and deeper. As a result, the person takes in a greater quantity of air and is thus able to extract the required amount of oxygen. He is breathing more deeply not because he particularly wants to, but because his body is telling him to do so. Therefore, this breathing is a reflex response over which he has no control. We conclude that if a mask to exclude oxygen can make you or me breathe more deeply, it could make a brain-injured child do the same.

The initial masking time is one minute. The child breathes into the mask and, when the mask is removed, his first reflex action will be to take a very deep breath.

This will be beneficial in two ways. First, the child has, for one minute, inhaled carbon dioxide, which causes the blood vessels to dilate; a greater volume of blood is therefore carried to the brain. Second, when the mask is removed, the first breath that the child takes is much deeper than usual, and thus more oxygen is taken in. This is then carried straight to the brain by the dilated blood vessels.

The results both in the UK and in the USA have far surpassed our hopes. We have seen children's lives saved because their breathing has improved and they have become less susceptible to respiratory illnesses. Their chest size has improved, fewer seizures have been noted, and increased alertness, less dribbling and better sensation in the extremities have been brought about by masking.

Although we have never had any injuries to children when this technique has been applied, it can be dangerous and *must never be attempted* in any way on your own child. We have deliberately avoided explaining the masking technique in great detail because it requires experience and knowledge to use it properly. We believe in the value of this technique because of one important fact: we have repeatedly seen it work.

Respiratory patterning

The technique that we use to regulate the pattern of breathing, or *respiratory patterning*, was developed in Philadelphia. It was realised at the Institutes for the Achievement of Human Potential that children unable to breathe regularly and efficiently might be remarkably improved if a way could be found to pattern their breathing, so that their brain would understand what it was like to breathe properly.

The basic ideas of respiratory patterning were worked out after a great deal of research in 1974–75. The results achieved have led us to develop respiratory patterning further. At first we noted that there is a high incidence among brain-injured children of incoordinate breathing. Some of the children suffer more problems when inhaling and some when exhaling. Two machines are used: the negative-pressure respiratory patterning machine is used to programme the brain with how it feels to breathe in and the positive-pressure machine is used to programme the brain with how it feels to breathe out.

Under medical supervision, the children on respiratory programmes are placed on whichever of these machines would benefit them most for up to three hours morning and afternoon. The heart rate and breathing rate are continuously monitored and recorded. In general, the children quickly adapt to the respiratory device and begin to breathe regularly for the first time in their lives. The children were being patterned while at rest, and we have now established to our satisfaction that we can improve a child's breathing while he is at rest. Unfortunately, the child may wish to move, and in some cases the child's breathing deteriorates once again but returns to a good level when he rests. Equipment has been, and is being, developed to programme the child's breathing while he is performing a task which will increase the body's need for oxygen.

Have you, if you have a brain-injured child, listened to his breathing and compared it with another child's? The difference is often quite remarkable. Breathing we all seem to take for granted! We challenge any of you to recite a nursery rhyme, sign a cheque or write a letter immediately after running up and down the stairs until you are utterly exhausted – even the simplest task becomes difficult until you have recovered. From our observations, respiratory patterning can lead to some of the following results, although this is not so in every case:

deep and regular breathing
warmer arms and legs
improved skin colour
improved health
an ability to chew as drooling reduces
improved swallowing
increased awareness
longer and deeper sleep
full alertness when awake
decrease in and sometimes stopping of seizures
increased control and volume of voice.

It is important to realise that respiratory machines are not the answer for all brain-injured children. In some cases the child has been so protectively sheltered by mum and dad that their breathing has never had a chance to develop. Children can easily develop some severe abnormalities in their posture, and this will also restrict their breathing. For some children, surgery will be necessary to straighten their limbs. However, this is undertaken only when everything else has been tried.

We live in an environment where there is much misunderstanding and myth and we have to live with many doctors who have closed minds. However, the tide does seem to be turning, especially as our programmes are based on common sense, understanding and logic. It appears to us that many of the medical profession do not understand the cause of the problem, only the symptoms. They therefore attempt to relieve or remove the symptoms but do not attempt to remove the cause. Our results in improving breathing lead us to assume that this type of programme is of major importance to many of our children. Sometimes the respiratory programme will involve swinging from overhead ladders, running, walking, cycling, swimming: in fact any form of exercise which would normally stress the respiratory system and thus make it work more efficiently. The type of respiratory programme will vary considerably, as do our children. Each programme is designed for each child's individual needs based on our experience, which is now considerable.

The importance of fluid control

Through observation and experience, we believe that the brain functions better in a low-fluid environment. What do we mean by that? We have already determined that all our children are brain-injured. It is also an accepted fact that damaged tissue collects fluid: for example, have you ever twisted your knee or sprained your ankle and seen it swell up? We have explained that brain-damaged children have a considerable number of dead, damaged or bruised brain cells. The fluid level within the skull of a brain-injured child is usually higher than that of a normal child.

Too much fluid in the skull is dangerous, because the amount of oxygen getting to the brain is controlled by the pressure on the brain, and the pressure on the brain is controlled by the amount of fluid around the brain. As the volume of fluid increases, the amount of oxygen getting to the brain decreases, because the skull is a closed, reasonably solid container, which cannot expand to accommodate extra volume. Along with others, we have determined that the brain functions better in a high-oxygen environment. We therefore believe that fluid control is very important, especially, in our experience, for children who suffer seizures.

Many brain-injured children have diets that are high in fluid content. This quite often occurs because parents can feed their child only with foods that are, for want of a better word, 'sloppy'. This can be for a variety of reasons:

1 The child is tube-fed because of breathing or swallowing problems, or because he is in a coma.
2 The child cannot chew.
3 Parents believe that this type of diet is what their child needs and wants, and they are also afraid of their child trying solids.
4 Parents have never been told to move their child on to solid foods and have relied wholeheartedly on the medical advice that they have received.
5 Some parents tend to quieten an irritable baby by allowing it to suck a bottle for greater lengths of time. It is also faster and simpler, in many cases, to feed a brain-injured child by bottle than by spoon.

Even if a child's diet is 'sloppy', the child might still be thirsty, especially if the diet contains carbohydrates (including sugar) or salt. Both of these items increase the need for fluid and the child therefore requires more drinks. As an example, place a container of table salt or sugar in the lounge or dining room and you will quickly see how they attract fluid.

We have deliberately avoided giving case histories or examples as this would, we believe, lead to comparisons being made and experiments being attempted. We understand the importance of fluid control but would like to point out that this is only one aspect of the therapy and will not work in isolation. We must stress that altering a child's fluid intake without proper knowledge and advice can have dire consequences, not only with brain-injured children but also with any child. Excessive fluid retention can be caused by problems in other organs, in particular the kidneys. If the kidneys cease to work properly this can lead to far too much fluid being retained or far too little, and in this case the kidney disease itself must be treated. Moreover, it is not simply a case of reducing what the brain-injured child drinks: the whole diet must be looked at, nutritional supplements prescribed if needed, and the total fluid intake in some cases reduced to a more normal level and in others very strictly controlled.

Each child has this part of his programme individually designed and tailored to his needs, the aim being to provide a healthy environment for the brain.

Chapter 11

Who is the best person to treat someone with brain injury?

By now you probably realise that we believe that parents and family are the best people to treat their child. This is at the moment contrary to most established practices, as many of the children that we see would, if the local authorities or social workers had their way, be in homes. Some of these homes are run by charitable organisations and some by local authorities. Within their terms of reference they probably perform their tasks to the best of their ability. It is our belief that the basic idea of putting children in homes is in most cases wrong. Naturally at the moment there is no other answer, and some people accept the inevitable because they also accept the advice of the people who perpetuate this system.

Come what may, the population of this country will, according to most estimates, decline and become top-heavy with older people. This means that every person who can work in any way will, in fact, be a useful member of society. It is our contention that most of the brain-injured children of today will become the brain-injured adults of tomorrow when they could, instead of being an unfortunate drain on our resources, be a useful addition to the nation's workforce. There will still obviously be a need for 'mental institutions' and homes for what we term 'brain-injured children'. This will be so because some people can handle a child but not an adult and are always worried by what happens when they, as parents, are dead.

We cannot turn every brain-injured child into a person who can function with his peers, but with our limited resources and knowledge we have managed to put some children into school and to prove that many of these children are educable and could eventually be useful members of society.

There are contentious statements in this book but we believe that parents with the right training and understanding are the best therapists. The main reason is that they love their child and are prepared to work far harder and longer than any professionally trained therapist. It is not hard to train parents and whether they are rich, poor, middle-class, black, white or yellow it matters not: they, if they want to, make the best therapists. The crux of the matter is the fact that many parents want to do something, but after years of searching they give up; some parents simply cannot cope anyway, and a home in these cases seems the obvious answer.

Homes for handicapped children do solve problems, but it must be remembered that they also create problems. The progress of children placed in homes, no matter how well they are now, is usually very limited and in some cases regression can occur. The personnel responsible for running these establishments are not numerous enough to cope with the children they have to look after. The cost of providing each child's place runs into thousands of pounds now, and this will escalate.

There are also several other problems in that these trained personnel cannot play the role of parents to every child. The children are also quite often suffering from a mixture of handicaps and are invariably likely to pick up bad habits quicker than good habits.

Parents who have children on our programmes, it is true,

are generally in receipt of standard government allowances and the cost of central and local governments is kept to this level. We have noted that, unfortunately, some parents have never been informed of all the allowances they are entitled to. The parents are not paid for their labours and receive no financial aid from us; in fact they pay us to help them. When the child is at an age when he or she should be in special school, parents with our help and guidance attempt to educate their child. Local authorities and social workers have put obstacles in the way of parents when they attempt this and consequently they receive very little financial support towards participating in our programmes even though the local authority may be saving several thousands of pounds.

It is true that some parents require substantial help from people outside the family. This is always forthcoming and it is amazing how many people can find an hour or two per week to help a brain-injured child. These helpers also receive no financial rewards and indeed are lucky if they get a cup of tea. The rewards that parents, family and helpers see are sometimes slow in coming, sometimes fast in coming and sometimes non-existent. Results obviously spur the effort, as does in some cases lack of results. No improvements for a long time means that our therapy is not working in this case, we do not know enough developmental science, we might not have taught the parents properly or they might not have done all that we asked.

Parents do not need expensive training courses and are quite capable of controlling and running a home programme. They spread the work throughout the day and can carefully control and monitor the daily situation. We can and do give developmental advice over the telephone but the usual medical problems are always looked after by the families' GPs who are nearly always most helpful and interested. Mum and dad love their child and are most easily in tune with their own child's problems, especially in respect of feeding, toiletry habits and so on. The child is also in a family atmosphere and environment which we believe to be a very important element in the success of our therapy.

Most of you who read this book will, we hope, realise that whilst we will continue our search for the answers and help as many children as we can, to help the great majority in the short term is an impossibility. There is one sure fact emerging consistently and that is parents are able to educate the supposedly uneducable and to help their child to improve functionally where they have been told improvement is impossible. They are, in our opinion, the heroes who are available night and day to help solve their child's problems.

Parents will also in our experience provide a very lucid report on their child for the very simple reason that they are part of the family. Parents have eyes and ears and, contrary to some viewpoints, are quite capable of critical observation. At a guess many of you who read this are parents of a brain-injured child and I wonder how many of you have ever had it suggested to you that you are capable of helping your hurt child. How wrong can people be: parents are the most precious asset not only in respect of normal children but even more so in the respect of a handicapped child. Parents, inadvertently perhaps, teach their well children to walk, talk, and so on. The list is endless. That being the case, they must be given the opportunity to do the same for their brain-injured child.

We feel that parents should at least have the option and this would obviously in time help relieve the pressure on our overworked National Health system. If you have ever visited special schools, day centres or homes, have you not wondered why the improving child is the exception to the rule? These institutions and homes are usually well run, scrupulously clean and in general very nice places, but they are not family homes and the teachers or house parents are not the true parents. It is a job, and a one to one relationship is impossible. In these circumstances it is possible to have happy brain-injured children and if that is the aim – fine! But for those who want to do something about these children we can make one statement.

We believe that the parents of a brain-injured child make the best therapists for their child.

Chapter 12

How do I get on programme?

By *on programme* we mean 'currently carrying out a programme designed and supervised by the Kerland Clinic'. So, how *do* you get on programme? The quick and simple answer is to say 'Contact the Kerland Child Development Centre'. So easy to say, but usually very difficult to do, the big question being how to get that address or telephone number, because it is often not provided by doctors, social workers or health visitors.

Another family in the same position as yourself might know. The advice and help given to families when their child is diagnosed as brain-damaged is significant by its absence, especially for those families who want to do something at home for their child. The number of families who want to find some possible extra help for their child is a small but growing percentage of the total. The response that families get when they ask for advice on alternative therapies varies considerably, but on the whole it is negative if not openly hostile. This naturally puts some families off approaching organisations such as ours because they have been taught to take heed of advice from professional people such as doctors, solicitors and teachers.

It takes some families hours and some families years to find the centre. The time taken appears to us to be relative to the frustration and desperation that parents feel in respect of what is being offered to them within the health, educational and social service systems.

Most families hear or read about our work when articles are published in local papers about children. One family cut an article out and Mum put it in her handbag – three months later she found it when turning her bag out. In the meantime her daughter had made no progress. Mum then rang us and after several letters and telephone calls, the family went on programme. One of the things this family did was to visit and talk to the family featured in the article. We like prospective new families to talk to families already on programme as we feel that they will ask questions of them that they will not initially ask us, and we are always happy to provide phone numbers. None of our families object to this since most of them went through the same procedure themselves and found it helpful. You may be interested to read the comments by a cross-section of families who have been on our programme in the appendix on p 162.

Another family was unofficially told of our existence by a health visitor and followed up with a letter, which led to a similar course of action as before, although in this case this family then experienced an upsurge in what the system could all of a sudden offer them. This is something which quite often happens, and it happens in a variety of ways:

More physiotherapy is offered.
More medical examinations and investigations are planned.
Places are made available in playgroups.
Social workers, health visitors and educational physio-therapists start taking greater interest.
The criticisms to alternative therapies start coming to the fore.

Time, as you know, is the enemy of a brain-injured child and the six months, one year, eighteen months delay that can be caused when the system gets to work can in some cases cause handicaps to worsen. After all, a year of our lives might not sound much but in the case of a two-year-old it is 50 per cent of his or her life.

The average age of a child when they go on programme is now far younger than it was ten years ago but the hurdles that you as parents have to overcome are just as hard if not harder than they were then. We also think it fair to say that as well as all these hurdles placed in front of them by others, families themselves experience a whole load of inner fears about going on programme. Every family has the same sort of fears but things that concern one family do not necessarily bother another. Some families worry about finding help, some worry about money, some worry about their own ability to cope with the change in lifestyle that naturally occurs. Some worry about equipment, some worry about the effect a programme will have on their family life and especially on any other children in the family.

These are just some of the added questions that you as a family must ask yourself once you have overcome the hurdles that will be placed in front of you by the system. These problems are very real: for example getting help can be almost impossible if you live in a farmhouse in the Brecon Beacons, but not if you live in a town. Mums and Dads have to become teachers of helpers and have to learn to run a timetable, and this is, for many, alien to their nature. Even if you live in a town the question of how to go about finding help can be frightening to some families. We try and talk about all of these problems and any others that may occur and to give what advice we can from all the experience we have had. Every family is different, their circumstances are different in every way and we do therefore take some time over providing this advice. Solution that suits one family does not suit another and so we have had to learn to be as flexible as possible.

We set great store by the parent's involvement with their

child and so from our first contact we set out to build and maintain a relationship revolving around truth and honesty. It has been known for us to advise a family that in their particular circumstances a programme is not, and will not provide, the answer to their problems. There must also be a good family relationship and both Mum and Dad must be committed to the idea of the programme. If only one parent is enthusiastic, the inevitable disruption to routine and sacrifices that have to be made will eventually lead to disagreement, which would be creating more problems than the programme was solving. How the work can be fitted into each family's life style depends on a whole host of variables, such as the amount of help available, the time when it is convenient and possible to work with your child, and the commitments that already exist. In many cases a different time has to be set aside each day, and much depends on time needed for playschool, school, nursery groups, physiotherapy, toddler group, swimming session, and so on.

However, having overcome the system's hurdles and having swallowed hard and worried about their own trepidations a family then writes for an appointment for an initial assessment and programme. The first visit lasts for two days and takes place at the Centre, where we have all the basic equipment. Generally we can give an appointment for an initial assessment within two to six weeks, a lot depending on whether the family require a specific two days or are able to settle for what is available. We do try to be flexible and to fit in where possible with what suits the family best. When the appointment is given our doctor will write to the child's GP for any relevant information.

From experience we believe that it is beneficial to deal with one family at a time, since we are then able to concentrate all our attention on them and their particular problems. It is important that two adults attend with the child, preferably Mum and Dad. However, this is not always possible, for example in the situation of a one-parent family, in which case we then ask that another adult come along, if possible one who is going to be very involved with the child and the programme. Some families have also brought a third person along, which is also fine by us.

Parents stay locally and attend the centre from 10 a.m. on both days – we provide them with a list of suitable local accommodation and sometimes other families already on programme will recommend somewhere to stay. The sequence of events upon arrival at the centre is the same in every case:

10 a.m. – 12.30 p.m. A full and comprehensive developmental history is taken to add to the information already obtained from the family's GP. A functional evaluation of the child is carried out.

12.30 p.m. – 2 p.m. The family go out to lunch.

2 p.m. – 2.30 p.m. The family is told the results of the evaluation and given a copy of their child's development graph.

2.30 p.m. – 5.30 p.m. A basic discussion then takes place concerning the philosophy behind our ideas and what a programme means in practical terms.

The topics covered are:

1 The philosophy behind our therapy
2 The problems likely to be encountered going on programme
3 Allowances and help available from central and local government
4 How to find and cope with the help from the community, which will be necessary to do the programme
5 Any other problems worrying the family; as you will

> now understand, these can vary enormously from
> family to family and yet be very similar

On the second day, at 10 a.m. the programme designed for your child will be shown to you, and will be run through twice during the morning with the centre's staff teaching the required techniques. Lunch is generally from noon to 2 p.m. on the second day, as both family and child are in need of a good rest. In the afternoon session the staff act as patterners and the family themselves run through their programme at least once and sometimes twice. Finally the staff will 'practise' any techniques until the parents are happy, and answer any further questions that have cropped up. Parents are given diagrams of any necessary equipment and handouts for patterners. It can also be possible to advise families on the availability of redundant equipment, which can help a family get into programme more quickly than would otherwise be possible.

The programme usually revolves around a sequence of activities lasting approximately thirty minutes, and we explain to families that it is in everyone's interest to build up to programme over a period of time. Time will fly for the family, and their lifestyle will change beyond recognition – as hopefully will their child, as his abilities improve and disabilities begin to disappear.

Chapter 13

What does the future hold?

Probably the first thing that we must do is to make more
families aware of the help and advice that is available to them
outside the health, educational and social service systems.
This is in itself a major task to be undertaken with caution
because as a result of our doing so more families will become
dissatisfied with what is on offer and will therefore look
outside the system for help.

We would like to think that this would reduce the burden
on an already overworked staff and thus hopefully make the
system more efficient. It is impossible to guess the numbers
of families who would look elsewhere for help – we suppose
the most that we could envisage is 10 per cent of the families concerned. This figure itself probably represents over
50,000 families, and we could only directly help a small
percentage of that number. What we can do is to try to
change the attitude of the professional workers towards this
type of therapy.

Undoubtedly this type of home stimulation therapy
achieves results, we believe far better results than in the 50s,
60s or 70s. The criticisms surrounding the original Doman-
Delcato therapies have never been properly answered, but
families still take their children there and they still get results.
We feel that we get better results because we have tried to
learn from experience. It is also true that we sometimes do

not get the progress we are looking for, although it is now very rare for a child not to improve in some way or other.

The criticism that is most often levelled is 'There has been no clinical trial to determine the effectiveness of this therapy.' We sometimes feel like using very strong language to the people who trot out this criticism. It just shows how little they know and understand about our work. We have listed just some of the variables that exist between the families that would make such a study virtually impossible:

1 Type of house.
2 Type of environment.
3 Abilities of parents.
4 Abilities of patterners.
5 Difference in lifestyles.
6 No child has exactly the same problems.
7 Programmes are individual.
8 Level of parental commitment is different.
9 No two families have the same backgrounds.
10 Parents view similar problems in different ways.

Each of these ten examples could be split again and again. Even if a clinical trial were possible, how could we design similar programmes for families knowing that in order to stand the best chance of being effective each programme must be individually tailored to the child and the family concerned? Of course, we could not. How many inventions, innovations, discoveries have been made and proven to be effective without the people concerned fully understanding in detail the reasons why something works? This list, too, is endless. Then there is also the list of medical discoveries where the doctor concerned has had to endure untold misery and vilification before his discoveries have been accepted. It is sad to say that this acceptance quite often does not occur in the lifetime of the discoverer.

The number of parents who will not accept that their child

has no future is growing, and it is becoming more and more important to be able to offer them a sensible alternative. We are not saying that all of the currently taught methods of handling the brain-damaged are wrong. They do get some results, and for the families who accept the level of those results and who are happy with what is offered then that is fine. The best teaching conditions are to be found where there is a one to one relationship between the teacher and the child. This is very difficult to achieve within current financial restraints and, in our opinion, will never be achieved. Parents worry that they are not helping their child enough – in many cases this is only because they do not know, or have not been shown, what to do.

We firmly believe that parents, if treated and taught properly, can help solve many of the problems that their children have. Treating the parents properly must start from the time of diagnosis of the child's problems. With birth injuries this is, in general terms, happening earlier in the child's life. As far as we can see there is no easy way to impart that sort of information, but it would take another book to write about the horrific ways in which some families are told of the child's problems. It is here that our task begins – with the doctors who handle the diagnosis and the follow-up service from then on. Only time will tell how successful or unsuccessful we have been. We also want to encourage families to set up self-help groups where they can not only participate in the follow-up service after diagnosis but can also indicate what they, as parents, find acceptable. The abilities of parents come to the fore when it is their brain-damaged child who needs help. We try hard to harness the desperation and frustration that parents feel and to change their usually negative attitude to one of a positive viewpoint. After all, we would all feel negative if we were told what our child would never do without even discussing what he might be able to do.

It is important that we change the attitude of many of those who work within the system to make them realise that we are not trying to prove them wrong or to take over their jobs: we are just trying to help, as indeed are they. Our techniques and attitudes might in some instances be similar, in others totally different, but the objective is the same. The demands of families usually far outweigh the supply of what is available and it is only organisations such as ours which can provide extra advice and help, and use the frustrations that you feel to the best advantage of your child.

Alongside trying to educate people about our work we also have to develop new ideas, research other therapies and in general keep looking for more and more different answers to the problems created by brain damage. One of the things that we must do over the years is to open other centres, the next one probably being in the Greater Manchester area. We expect such centres will be small and self-contained, and run by staff trained at Taunton.

From long experience people who want to work in this field do not just appear, they evolve. The wages are criminally low and the hours exceedingly long, but the rewards in terms of job satisfaction just cannot be measured. We are continually looking for potential staff members but we are, and always will be, very selective – although only in the way that will ensure that the people who join us are certain that this is what they want to do with their lives.

Our best advertisement is happy families, doing our programme and getting results. If that did not happen, you would not be reading this book. Our future existence depends on our continuing ability to achieve results, and one of the ways to assist this is to provide families with access to the latest medical technology. For example, we are currently attempting to raise the funds necessary to purchase, install and run the latest sophisticated magnetic resonance brain and body scanner. Many of our families have difficulty in persuading doctors to recommend a brain scan especially if the child has been known to be brain-damaged for some years. It is our aim to have our children scanned in this way at least every year. We do not yet know exactly what we will find to eventually help us to provide better programmes and a better service, but what we do know is that such scans will help us understand more about the effectiveness or noneffectiveness of programmes. It cannot really be called a research project but more of a search project.

We sincerely hope that the incidence of brain injury in babies will reduce as medical knowledge increases, and we fully accept that the best solution is prevention. However significantly this number is reduced, though, there will always be a call for our services. The incidence of brain damage caused by an accident in the home increases as a family's overall standards of living improve. For example, as more and more homes in the more affluent areas of the USA have swimming pools then there are more children suffering brain damage from drowning accidents. The same principle of treatment can also be applied to adults who have suffered brain damage as a result of a stroke or a road accident. The problem with treating adults is that there are always more people who are prepared to help a two-year-old brain-damaged child than will help a fifty-five-year-old who has had a stroke and is suffering similar symptoms to that of the child.

We would eventually like to think that this therapy will be available to any family who want it. It would be nice if part or all of the cost would be met by the NHS but I am sure that, simple as that might sound, bureaucracy and 'informed opinion' will at best make this a very long term possibility.

To most parents the future is not just bleak for their brain-damaged children, it is horrifying. When we see children (who were formerly written off) walk, talk, see, run, read and write, we must continue our work. You as parents will have to fight for everything for your child because you want the best for them and their future. So do we.

Conclusion

As you will recall, all the basic philosophies regarding the treatment described in this book emanated from Philadelphia. However, after several years of observation and work in the field of brain damage we came to what we felt were sensible conclusions in respect of this type of home programme:

1 The basic philosophies and principles of treatment are effective when used properly.
2 In our opinion the application of these principles should be flexible and should take into account the total environment within which they are being used.
3 As far as the UK is concerned many, although by no means all, of the criticisms previously levelled at this type of home therapy were justified.
4 We see no valid reason why this type of treatment must always be used to the exclusion of all others. We have no wish to fight the system; we feel strongly that there is a place for this form of therapy alongside schooling, physiotherapy, and so on.

Using these conclusions as a guideline, when we set up the Kerland Child Development Centre in March 1982 we decided on the following course of action:

1 To send staff to visit the family's own home, since invariably the child performs better in familiar surroundings and we see at first hand the environment in which the family are working and the problems facing them.

2 In most cases to reduce the length of the programme to bring about the necessary progress while allowing time for play, school if required, or outings – in other words, normal life.

3 To look at the programme as only part of the family's way of life and to avoid letting it take over.

4 To offer help to anyone who had suffered brain damage, regardless of age.

5 Possibly the most important point of all – to retain flexibility in everything we do.

Whilst we will always tell a family how much we think they should be doing with their child, at the end of the day the decision about how much they actually do must be theirs and theirs alone.

Since we have adopted this approach we have found that we are no longer at war with 'the system'. If we can all work alongside each other, then surely the child must have the best possible chance of success. Some people will say that this makes it impossible to say what specifically has brought about the progress – but if you were the parents of a brain-injured child, would you really care as long as progress is being made?

Since writing the bulk of this book, we have modified our assessment criteria. Although we still look closely at a child's tactile awareness, and where necessary incorporate tactile stimulation into the programme, we no longer feel that this is one of the major areas of development. We do, however, feel that two areas of major importance have been sadly neglected, and so have added them to our assessment procedures. They are the areas of self-help and socialisation. We would feel that we had not done a child any favours if we taught him to walk, talk, read and write – but then he could not think for himself, look after himself or mix with others. If this were the case, surely he would be just as much an outsider to society, even possibly labelled 'freak', as he would be if he could not do anything.

Play is an essential part of development in children, and we feel that it is important that brain-injured children should also be given time to learn how to play. It is sad to see a child who at the age of ten has to be taught how to play because until then his life has revolved around hard work. Similarly, it is important that if we are helping a child to develop and acquire new skills, he must have time to experiment with those skills and apply them to everyday life. After all, there is more to running than just having the ability to do so – there are races to be won and footballs to be chased.

There are a growing number of families who want to, and are prepared to, work at home with their brain-injured children in order to achieve as much progress as they possibly can, but who at the same time do not want to resign from 'the system'. We believe that our application of this form of treatment offers a solution to these families. We cannot, and would not, ever offer any guarantee that the programme will work – some children respond very well in a short time, others make very little progress in exchange for months or years of very hard work. From our experience, however, it is a rare parent who regrets the time spent on doing a programme. To quote one parent:

'Even though my child did not make a lot of progress, I feel satisfied that I have done everything I can to give her a chance.'

Appendix

In order to give you a view from some of the families who have been on our programme, we decided to ask a cross-section to provide us with comments. They were asked six basic questions:

1 Why did you turn to the Kerland Clinic?
2 What other therapies have you used or looked at?
3 Do you think programme/patterning was worthwhile?
4 How did it affect the family?
5 What did local professionals say about the programme?
6 Do you think that there is enough information made available by the NHS about alternative therapies?

We hope that you find their answers interesting.

Thomas and Victoria

Why did you turn to the Kerland Clinic?
We went on programme because we were desperate to do something for our two children. No one else had offered us any practical help or suggestions, except a very limited level of physiotherapy and respite care if we could no longer cope.

What other therapies have you used or looked at?
At the time (and since) we investigated any form of formal or

informal therapy which we felt might offer something. This has included speech therapy, the Peto Clinic, homeopathy, the use of Macaton, and special diets.

Learning of any other treatment, palliative or therapeutic, and understanding its rationale has had several benefits, even if we have later decided that it does not work (in our case). It has helped us to clarify what can appear a bewildering array of thoughts and hopes. It has helped us assure ourselves that we have done everything that we can to help our children. (Whilst we do not feel guilty about the children's condition, we would feel guilty about not doing all we could to help them overcome it.) The more knowledgeable we become generally about medical matters, the more confidence we have had in dealing with the medical profession, and hence a greater willingness has been shown to accept our assertions and requests. An illustration of this is that after persisting in attending annual clinics at the Hammersmith for several years with no benefit, this year some blood tests were suggested that have shown that the children have a condition called 'carbohydrate-deficient glycoprotein syndrome', which resulted in the cerebellar hypoplasia, and so another door opens.

What did local professionals say about the programme?
We were met initially by some scepticism by many in the medical profession, a knee-jerk reaction which is displayed less and less as the children progress. It seems that the younger the professional, the more open his or her mind.

It has been a constant source of frustration to us that the credibility of an institution seems directly proportional to the amount of media coverage gained by the institution concerned, followed closely by the allocation of funds from various bureaucracies.

Steve Byrne, Okehampton

Brain Damage: Don't learn to live with It!

Anna Marie

Why did you turn to the Kerland Clinic?
After Anna Marie's illness which turned her from a normal child into a severely brain-damaged child, we felt we needed to do something positive. We heard about the Kerland Clinic from a parent in the hospital. We went on programme to stimulate her and do as much as we could to improve her helpless body.

What other therapies have you used or looked at?
We took Anna Marie to the Bobath Centre in London to try and ease her severe spasms. This proved ineffective.

Do you think that programme/patterning was worthwhile?
Over the last seven years on programme with Anna, we have had some major disappointments, but overall we think it has been worthwhile.

How did it affect the family?
The programme has become part of our family life. The children have grown up with this way of life, and we feel over the years the programme is part of our everyday life.

What did local professionals say about the programme?
Our doctor and health visitor have very little to do with Anna Marie and never mention anything (only about her health). The physiotherapist is always concerned and worries whether we are going to harm her joints. Although Anna has been on programme for seven years the physio is still against what we do. Anna's teacher and deputy head of her school are becoming more interested in what we are doing at home and at the Clinic, and I think they are more positive than negative about Anna Marie's programme.

Do you think that enough information is made available by the NHS?
We do not think there is enough information; we are left to find out everything on our own. They don't think it is worth treating brain-damaged children: this is what we found.

Martin and Wendy Davies, Cambridge

Andrew

Andrew is doing really well at school; he is in the Juniors now and has settled down very quickly. We were amazed at how smoothly the transfer went – the LEA didn't even argue about it! He sat the seven-year-old SATs at the end of last term and came out at level 2 on everything. He was only exempted from handwriting (for obvious reasons). The school were told by a special needs advisory teacher that Andrew is working at a higher level than any other child of his age with similar disability in the country. So we all felt very proud of him and are delighted that all our fight to keep him in mainstream had been justified. We are looking forward to a peaceful few years until we have the battle for senior school!

Why did you turn to the Kerland Clinic?
By the time Andrew was eighteen months old it was becoming increasingly obvious to us that (a) he was very bright, (b) he had a lot of problems with his motor skills and (c) the physio-therapist would not accept that he was bright, nor was the type of therapy (Bobath) that she was offering helping Andrew to overcome his physical disability. Her whole attitude was 'negative', dwelling on what he could not do rather than on what he might be able to do given the opportunity. It didn't help that Andrew hated the sight of her either!

We decided to go to the Kerland having seen the progress that another local child had made in a very short while on her patterning programme.

What other therapies have you used or looked at?
To start with Andrew was being treated by a physiotherapist
and an occupational therapist, using mainly Bobath techniques. We had looked at conductive education but felt that
it would be far too disruptive both for Andrew and for his
sister Sarah to have to go to Hungary. We rejected the idea
of going to Philadelphia for the same reason.

Andrew continued to have good occupational and speech
therapy cover while he was on programme. However the
physiotherapy was withdrawn for several years as the physio
didn't approve of the Kerland's methods.

Andrew did have physio for the last eighteen months or
so that he was on programme, but we had to go to another
hospital for it. Since he came off programme in December
1991, he has continued to have weekly physiotherapy, some
speech therapy and visits from the occupational therapist. I
still don't feel that this is enough so we do daily stretching
exercises before he gets up that are a mixture of patterning
(hip unlocking) and physiotherapy. He also has fortnightly
aromatherapy which he loves and I feel does him far more
good than the physiotherapy. At the end of his massage he
is completely relaxed and is able to do far more than he can
at the end of physiotherapy.

Do you think that programme/patterning was worth while?
Yes – or we would not have carried on for five years.

Andrew is a fit and healthy child; he rarely suffers from
chest infections entirely because, I am sure, of years of
masking and respiratory patterning. His speech only began
to develop properly when we started respiratory patterning
and, even though we no longer pattern, he still has good
control over his breathing whilst speaking.

Although Andrew didn't progress as far as we had hoped
physically, he is very strong in his legs. We feel his lack
of progress had as much to do with his general lack of

motivation as it did with any real inability to do things. In fact, if we have one criticism about the patterning it is that for a child like Andrew the programme does not seem to provide enough incentive to motivate them. He would perhaps have been better working in a group with some element of competition.

How did it affect the family?
Possibly the person who could have been most adversely affected by the programme and the amount of effort that it took was Sarah. She was certainly very jealous of all the attention that Andrew had when she was younger but now she is old enough to understand that he is always going to need more of our time, I don't think that the patterning has had any long-term effect on her. The majority of the patterning went on while she was at school and we tried to let her do all the normal after-school activities, although we had to rely on her friends' parents to do a lot of the running around for us that this normally entails. The only time that the patterning really put a strain on family life was when we had to do it at weekends as well, once Andrew started school.

What did local professionals say about the programme?
We have been fairly lucky over the years in that, apart from the first physiotherapist that Andrew had, the majority of the professionals have been very interested and supportive. The GP that we are 'assigned' to isn't particularly interested so we normally try to see another member of the practice who is. Our present physiotherapist is great and believes that parents know best, as do the occupational therapist and speech therapist. In fact, the latter was really quite amazed at the difference in Andrew's breathing and speech once he started respiratory patterning and I think it made her think very carefully about how she would treat children with similar problems in future. The paediatrician, Dr Gabriel,

is also very supportive of parents who want to try alternative therapies.

Do you think that enough information is made available by the NHS?
Definitely not! I think that, as with everything, parents need to be given as much information as possible on all the options available for them to be able to make the right decision about what is best for their child. It should not be left to the professionals, as I believe that parents are the only real 'experts' on a specific child.

Sue Bird, St Albans

Adam

Why did you turn to the Kerland Clinic?
We first went on programme because it was wonderful to see the progress other children were making (after watching news reports on this treatment). We had to do something for our son; we could not just leave him a 'cabbage', as was diagnosed.

What other therapies have you used or looked at?
We were getting only twenty minutes physiotherapy a week from the Health Service, so we looked for something else. We looked into Peto but we did not want Adam to go away. To be honest, until we found the Kerland there was nothing else we could find in the way of treatment for Adam.

Do you think that programme/patterning was worthwhile?
The treatment we have been giving Adam at the Kerland has literally changed his future. He became our little boy again; he is aware, less stiff and doing things we never dreamed

he could achieve. It has certainly been worthwhile to us as a family.

How did it affect the family?
The Kerland programme has definitely changed us. Although there are only Adam, Mark and I, we have been brought much closer together because we all work together. We don't argue so much now and find refuge in helping Adam to reach his full potential. Family life is obviously different but I am sure for the better. We are not so isolated, as we have many friends now, and certainly don't have time to think about tomorrow, let alone ten years from now.

What did local professionals say about the programme?
Our doctors were all against this treatment. We were told the usual: it was 'false hope' and 'he would have achieved this anyway'; 'have another baby and forget Adam'; 'perhaps put him in a home because you will have no life'. All we got really was no hope and a negative future.

Do you think that enough information is made available by the NHS?
Everything we have done for Adam in the way of helping him has been found by us. There was no information about alternative therapy for Adam available. When we left hospital we found ourselves very alone and abandoned until we started to talk to friends and other people, who told us they had heard of 'this or that', so we looked things up.

Ruth Briner, South Ascot

Carys

Why did you turn to the Kerland Clinic?
Once Carys had come home from hospital and we had
adjusted our lives back into a routine we heard about the
Kerland Centre. We decided to go on programme because
if we wanted any quality of life for Carys it was up to us to
do what we could for Carys.

What other therapies have you used or looked at? We looked
at a couple of different therapies before we heard about the
Kerland Centre. We looked at the Peto Institution and the
British Brain Institute.

Do you think that programme/patterning was worthwhile?
We both feel that what we have achieved from the therapy
is already quite a lot and Carys has made remarkable
progress.

How did it affect the family?
I suppose it has affected us as a family. It has taught us all
that we have a responsibility and commitment to Cary's
daily routine. We have learnt to adjust family life around
it. In some ways it has brought us more closer together.
The only bad points that I can really think of is knowing
you have to be home at certain times of the day for Cary's
patterning, but at the end of the day we know it is for her
own good.

What did local professionals say about the programme?
The National Health Service disagreed with the programme
from the very beginning and said we were wasting our time
and money and it would do Carys no good at all. The
doctors and physiotherapists have now admitted Carys has
made some progress with the programme.

Do you think that enough informations is made available by the NHS?
The National Health Service has never told us about any centres such as the Kerland apart from their own.

Jane and Alan Saif, Barry

Nicola

Why did you turn to the Kerland Clinic?
Although Nicola was slow it was not until fifteen months that we realised there might be a problem. Shortly before her second birthday she was diagnosed as having 'severe learning difficulties'. At that stage, although Nicola could sit upright and bottom shuffle, she could not move if placed on her back or tummy and could not begin to walk or even crawl. The staff at the local hospital were very kind and understanding, but were unable to provide any kind of practical help to help Nicola, other than a one-hour weekly visit from a physiotherapist, which was more of a social call, to check on the family welfare.

We felt Nicola clearly had potential to improve her mobility, but we needed to be shown how, so that we could teach her, rather than just waiting to see if she would walk or not. After seeing an article in a magazine about a little boy who had been helped by the Kerland (who we had never heard of), we rang the Kerland to find out more . . .

Within three months of finally being told by the hospital of their diagnosis, and not knowing if she would ever walk or talk, we went to the Kerland for an initial visit. We had already come to the quick conclusion that, however nice and understanding staff within the NHS are, the NHS simply does not have the resources (either time or money) to cope with the needs of the handicapped.

Within an hour of our visit to the Kerland the feeling

171

of relief was simply enormous. Just to be with people who were specialists, were going to spend the whole day with us – and we were having their sole attention. After the usual NHS experience of delayed appointments, endless waiting in hospital waiting-rooms, just to be seen on time at the Kerland immediately made a lasting impression and, within the hour, we knew Nicola was in the right place.

What other therapies have you used or looked at?
Only one, the British Institute for Brain-Injured Children, but we felt their programme was too intensive and not flexible enough.

Do you think that programme/patterning was worthwhile?
Undoubtably yes. Within a few months of starting programme, Nicola's mobility had improved greatly and she was far more alert. After eleven months she started to walk quite well unaided and do most of the things a normal child can. Her speech is, however, limited but we are working on it.

How did it affect the family?
With another daughter, Sarah, four years older than Nicola, our major concern over the programme was how it would disrupt the family life. Once we were up and running, however, it was surprising how quickly a routine developed. As far as possible, we tried to ensure that the exercises had finished by the time Sarah had come home from school so that a normal amount of time was spent with her.

We feel that the effect of Nicola's lack of progress by not going on programme would have placed a far greater strain on us than the effects of a new routine.

What did local professionals say about the programme?
The reactions were, in a word, mixed. Most acknowledge the progress Nicola has made, but often the response is that she

would have walked one day anyway. The major concern of most was the effect the programme would have on us all and that, whilst our motives were good, it would place too much of a strain on the whole family.

Do you think that enough information is made available by the NHS?
Any information obtained is what we ourselves have sought out; it is not readily available. We were not given any information or details on alternative treatments by the local profession.

Mr and Mrs Tilley, Lincoln

Nigel

At nineteen years of age Nigel is a very independent, strong-willed teenager. This, however, has not always been the case. When Nigel was a baby we were told by the medical profession that his progress was very poor. Suffering from cerebral palsy, he would always need feeding, would always be incontinent, and would never be able to sit unsupported, never mind ever walking. His future seemed very bleak indeed.

Why did you turn to the Kerland Clinic?
We heard about a revolutionary treatment available in Philadelphia, USA. As we were unable to obtain any effective therapy for Nigel in this country, we decided, against the advice of doctors, to travel to Philadelphia and see what they had to offer us. This was a journey that was to have a significant effect on the life of not only Nigel but also his three sisters, two of whom were not born at that time. We came home from the USA armed with a therapy programme to carry out at home, lots of enthusiasm and a whole host

of friends and neighbours who were willing to give of their time to help us carry out the programme. Within a week of returning home we were in full swing, carrying out our programme and feeling optimistic about Nigel's future for the first time in four years.

By the time we were due for our first three-monthly assessment we had already noticed several significant changes in Nigel and were very eager to make the journey down to Somerset to meet Margaret, who was to take over the management of Nigel's programme in this country to save us having to travel to the USA every three months. We continued on programme for several years, initially seven days a week, but as Nigel improved we spent less time doing exercises and more time going out and about to such activities as swimming and visiting places of interest, which Nigel had taken no interest in before going on programme. I cannot say that Nigel's progress was spectacular: more a case of sheer dogged persistence bringing about results. Patterning was a nightmare, with very little co-operation from Nigel. Spatial awareness activities were great fun, with lots of laughter and very popular with Nigel. Ladder work was also very popular but breathing exercises were considered a bore.

Do you think programme/patterning was worthwhile?
These years of perseverence paid off, and Nigel's life became transformed and more fulfilling. At nineteen years of age Nigel leads a very busy life. He attends the school of learning support at a local college where he is learning independence skills. From a toddler unable to do anything and who screamed every time Mum went out of his line of vision, he is now a very active teenager. In recent years he has been camping with the Scouts and had been on activity holidays to Norfolk, the Lake District and France. His favourite activities include swimming, horse riding, canoeing and abseiling. Not only can he now feed himself (with a knife

174

and fork!) but he can also make himself a hot drink and snacks such as sandwiches and toast. He can wash and dress himself and even hand-wash and iron his own clothes. He has also made several useful articles in his woodworking class, including a very sturdy coffee table. He is able to walk with the aid of a rollator and values his mobility very highly.

How did it affect the family?
Of course the intervening years have not always been easy. As Nigel has three sisters, one eighteen months older than himself and the other two ten years and seven years younger, it has been very hard going at times, especially as the younger ones were born while Nigel was still on programme. We were warned by the doctors that being on programme would have an adverse effect on our marriage and family life. Well, I'll let the facts speak for themselves. We have just celebrated our silver wedding anniversary – so no problem there. As for our daughters, being on programme meant that we were able to organise our own lives, with, for example, one clinic appointment every three months instead of three hospital appointments every week. This enabled us to do the programme when it suited us, around family outings and such like.

Our daughters have always been very helpful and, when not being involved in helping with the programme, could be found patterning their soft toys and dolls and even on occasions the family cat! Our eldest daughter, Yvonne, spent eighteen months working in special education. After this she was so disillusioned with her job that she moved down to Somerset and is now training with Margaret and Trevor to become a human developmentalist. Our other two daughters are both very caring and very understanding of the needs of the disabled. Although still very young, they both spend their spare time giving voluntary help in a holiday home for handicapped people. Being on programme has had a beneficial effect on all our family and, I think, made us better, more caring people.

Mr and Mrs Finney

Natalie

Why did you turn to the Kerland Clinic?
Natalie is on the programme because the theory behind the treatment made sense to us, and nothing anyone had done with Natalie before did. The programme is treating the cause of Natalie's problem, the brain, whereas the conventional physiotherapist was treating the symptoms. It is Natalie's best chance of achieving her potential, and can be done in her own home with those she loves and trusts around her, allowing a 'normal' lifestyle to be enjoyed too.

Her community physiotherapist was offering her one forty-five-minute session once a week – excluding school holidays! – and despite having asked repeatedly for a set of exercises to be shown to me to carry out on Natalie, I was constantly told that it was not any specific exercise or the repetition of exercises that would help her. Well, Natalie still has cerebral palsy during the school holidays, and by opting for the Kerland Programme we knew she was getting the help she needed because there were reasons for each exercise and why it was carried out. The programme deals with the 'whole' child, whereas what we had been offered by conventional methods involved one person looking at Natalie's posture, one looking at function and another looking at speech. Then there were those who just came and looked! No-one had ever looked at her as a whole before, and many of those who did come contradicted each other, leaving us totally confused.

What other therapies have you used or looked at?
We read a little into conductive education methods of

treatment, and our reasons for very quickly deciding it was not suitable are as follows:

1 The cost of it financially would be beyond us.
2 We were not prepared to take Natalie away from her home, family and those she loved to go to Hungary (if she were accepted) as we feel that a stable background is essential to her if she is to grow up learning to cope with cerebral palsy and be well-adjusted.
3 We felt that it would put a tremendous strain on us as parents and on our marriage. It was not something we were prepared to risk – the break-up of our marriage – as Natalie's problems were enough in themselves without more, and she needed her parents together, not apart.
4 We did not feel that conductive education made as much sense as the Kerland Programme, although we do realise that many children have been helped by this method.

We have taken Natalie for cranial osteopathy, which we feel has helped her breathing, but the programme has helped her breathing too, so we feel the osteopathy has complemented the programme, and in no way is responsible solely for Natalie's progress. It has helped clear her lungs and sinuses. We took her after she had been on the programme for five months and were told by the osteopath that it would help the programme be more effective. It has helped to relax her body.

How did it affect the family?
It affected us in many ways. As Natalie's mother, it has helped me to overcome much of the guilt I felt for Natalie having cerebral palsy, as now I am doing something positive about it and achieving results beyond our expectations in such a short time.

We are exhausted: we are more determined than ever for Natalie and for what she will achieve. Things in the home that mattered before no longer do – who cares if the floor needs mopping or the room needs dusting if Natalie can now crawl upstairs? It has given us a new set of values and put a new perspective on life. I tell all the patterners that I will never apologise for the state of the house – the house can wait but Natalie can't. We thrive on chaos and are stronger and closer for it, as a family.

We are more positive than ever about her condition. We wanted to be before the Programme but were afraid to be because of the attitudes of the 'professionals'. It has given us confidence and, more importantly, it has given Natalie confidence. It has made us feel wonderful to know that we were right about Natalie's capabilities. We have only been able to prove it with the help of the Kerland Clinic.

The help of the Clinic has made us more disgusted than ever with the treatment and attitudes of the NHS. It has made us quite cynical about the medical profession, who think we are peculiar for exploring Natalie's potential the way we are.

Financially, we are worse off – but what rewards! For every negative comment I could make about how the programme has affected us I can think of two to cancel it out. All I need to do is to look at our little girl and the negatives disappear. She is a joy to see!

What did local professionals say about the programme?
I asked a doctor at Alder Hey, Liverpool, what he thought about the fact that we were considering bringing Natalie to the Kerland Clinic and his very words were 'Don't waste your time and money, my dear'. Having rapidly formed an opinion regarding him on my first meeting with him, my instincts told me to do the opposite of what he said!

The health visitor said: 'I really hope that you are not

going to pin all your hopes for Natalie on this Clinic, as you could be very disappointed.' I told her I saw no reason for disappointment.

The paediatrician said: 'This kind of therapy has no medium- or long-term benefit to the child – Natalie would have done all this anyway.' We cannot agree with her.

Our GP has been very interested in and supportive of what we have done on the programme with Natalie. She puts her progress down to the input she has had from us with the Clinic's help.

The portage worker has been very supportive and interested even though Natalie no longer receives portage. She is very open-minded and wishes that more children were given the opportunity of the Kerland Programme.

Generally the professionals (with a few exceptions) show a reserved interest in what we are doing, and their attitudes tend to be very patronising regarding the Clinic. We feel as if we are banging our heads against a brick wall. Several of them say they will read further into the methods used by the Kerland, but few do, as far as we know.

Something else we have noticed is that if we are giving Natalie input at home, then we tend not to get the input from the community to which we are entitled. We are not sure if this is because they think that Natalie's needs are being met by us, or because they do not want to work with or for a child who is receiving alternative therapy. The attitude of the professionals seems to be that if it suits them and their timetable, then it's fine. They do not often have the needs of the child at heart. It would appear that they will get the child to an acceptable level (to their way of thinking) and one that is cost-effective – *most* important! – and their job is done.

It amazes us that even a body like the Spastics' Society do not fully recognise or appreciate the work of the Clinic. They are not very forthcoming regarding their support for your work. We wish professionals were in their jobs because they want to help these children, and not for the pay-cheque at the end of the month. There is a distinct lack of dedication.

Do you think that programme/patterning was worthwhile?
Quite simply, yes!

At Christmas Natalie could not even crawl. By May she was crawling in cross-pattern. By June she could walk whilst pushing her truck. She could crawl upstairs and get down again. Natalie climbed up on a chair, stood up and toppled over – her first real 'bump' – and we were delighted: She tried to stand up on her bed and has a dreadful bruise on her nose – we are proud of it! These are all things that able-bodied children do and parents moan about and take for granted. To us they are a sign of her ability and progress, and only achieved since being on the Kerland Programme.

Natalie has now been given the opportunity of a place in mainstream nursery without a statement. We are delighted, as it gives us chance to see how she copes there and what her needs will be by the time she is eligible for full-time school. I have to say that I would be quite prepared to keep Natalie out of school to continue her Programme, as I feel that if we look back when she is ten years old and ask 'What did Natalie benefit from most at four or five years; was it the opportunity of mobility, or the opportunity of school?', the answer would be mobility.

So it has been worth while.

Do you think that enough information is made available by the NHS?
We found information hard to come by. We found out because we sent off for information from the Spastics' Society, read books, and talked to as many different people as possible. At the hospital it was a question of here is the physiotherapist, and she will see Natalie each week (if we

were lucky) and that was the end of it. There was never any discussion about anything else.

There is not enough coverage of alternative treatment given in the media and I think this is because – generally speaking – what the children are suffering from in the way of brain-injury is not life-threatening. Medical stories that capture the headlines tend to be dramatic, because they are. I think our children belong to a forgotten race.

Glossary

Cross-patterning A patterning technique that involves moving the left arm and right leg forward and then the right arm and left leg forward.

Masking The technique of excluding oxygen for a short while, causing the masked person to breathe deeply when the mask is removed.

Neurological organisation The concept that the brain develops in a structured and orderly fashion, successfully passing through each stage of development in turn, as a result of appropriate stimulation.

On programme Currently carrying out a programme developed and supervised by the Kerland Clinic.

Patterners The parents, partners, carers and volunteers who help the brain-damaged person carry out a programme of patterning.

Patterning Programming the damaged brain with the knowledge of how it feels to carry out certain actions.

Respiratory patterning The method of teaching a brain-injured person to breathe efficiently using machines that help him to exhale or inhale.

Trunkal patterning A patterning technique that involves curling up and straightening out the body.

Recommended Reading List

What to Do about Your Brain-Injured Child. G. Doman (1988). The Better Baby Press, Philadelphia, PA.

Brain-Injured Children. E. W. Thomas (1969). Charles C Thomas, Springfield, Ill.

Human Neurological Organisation. E. B. LeWinn (1969). Charles C. Thomas. Springfield, Ill.

Children's Minds. M. Donaldson (1978). Fontana.

Is My Child Hyperactive? J. Douglas (1991). Penguin Books.

Allergies and the Hyperactive Child. D. J. Rapp (1988). Thorsons Publishing Group.

The Growth and Development of Children, 4th edn, C. Lee (1990). Longman.

Coma Arousal: The Family as a Team. E. B. LeWinn (1985). Doubleday & Company, Inc. New York.

Head Injury and Coma: how you can help. W. D. Clarke & J. Sheridan, National Head Injuries Association.

Not All in the Mind. R. Markarness (1990). Pan Books.

More Than Sympathy. The everyday needs of sick and handicapped children and their families. R. Lansdown (1980). Taverstock Publications.

Children of Dreams, Children of Hope. R. Veras (1985). The Better Baby Press, Philadelphia, PA.

Todd. D. Melton (1985). The Better Baby Press, Philadelphia, PA.

The Spiritual Life of Children. R. Coles (1990). Harper Collins.

Understanding Child Intelligence. P. Lawrence (1988). Robinson Publishing, London.

Down's Syndrome: An Introduction for Parents. C. Cunningham (1982). Human Horizons Series. Condor Book, Souvenir Press.

Your Growing Child: From Birth to Adolescence. D. Fontana (1990). Fontana/Collins.

The Vitamin Bible. E. Mindell (1985). Arlington Books.

Brain Injury: Tapping the Potential Within. I. Hunter (1987) Ashgrove Press Ltd.